New Music Horizons

Fourth Book

ILLUSTRATED BY JULES GOTLIEB

McCONATHY

MORGAN

MURSELL

BARTHOLOMEW

BRAY

MIESSNER

BIRGE

SILVER BURDETT COMPANY

NEW YORK CHICAGO SAN FRANCISCO

ACKNOWLEDGMENTS

The authors are indebted to so many music educators for their interest and cooperation that space prohibits individual acknowledgment of their valued contribution.

To the following composers and publishers from whom source materials have been secured, credit and appreciation are due:

The American Folklore Society, Inc., for "Bright Fire In Your Eyes" and "Lullaby" from *Spanish American Folk Songs*, collected by Eleanor Hague.

D. Appleton-Century Company for permission to reprint the words of "Elephants" by Lenore M. Link, "The Little Elf" by John Kendrick Bangs, and "The Squirrels' Thanksgiving" by Frank H. Swett.

L. H. Bailey for the words of "The Summer Wind" from *Wind and Weather*.

Marjorie Barrows and the Whitman Publishing Company for permission to reprint the words of "The Pine Tree" from *Two Hundred Best Poems for Boys and Girls*.

Paul Burlin for permission to reprint "Okum Daagya" and "Aotzi No-otz" from *The Indians' Book*, recorded and edited by Natalie Curtis, published by Harper & Brothers.

Claude Champagne for "Tell Me, Shepherdess."

The Christian Science Monitor for the words of "Chestnut Babies" by Mabel Livingstone.

The Estate of Stella Marek Cushing for selected materials from Czechoslovakia, Holland, Moravia, Russia, Sweden, and Yugoslavia.

Hilda E. Dierker for Pipe and Drum Pieces from Mexico and accompanying photograph.

Oliver Ditson Company for permission to reprint "An Old Fairy Tale" from *60 Folk Songs of France* by Tiersot.

Helen Hartness Flanders and Arthur Wallace Peach for "Jolly Old Roger" from *A Garland of Green Mountain Song*, copyright by the Committee of Traditions and Ideals of the Vermont Commission of Country Life.

Nora Flynn for "Go to Sleep, My Baby Child."

Follett Publishing Company for permission to reprint the words of "A Modern Dragon" from *Songs Around a Toadstool Table* by Rowena Bastin Bennett.

The Grade Teacher for the words of "Shadow Pictures" by Anna M. Priestly.

Vida L. Guiterman for "Amen," first published in *Classmate*.

Herbert Halpert for "Drovers' Song," recorded by Ina Jones, Nellie Prewitt, and Vivian Skinner, and "We're Going Round the Mountain," recorded by a group of children from Brandon, Mississippi.

Harcourt, Brace and Company, Inc., for permission to reprint "The Road" from *Magpie Lane* by Nancy Byrd Turner, copyright, 1927.

Marguerite Haven for Flute Tunes from China.

Houghton Mifflin Company for permission to reprint the words of "The Bird's Nest" from *All About Me* by John Drinkwater.

Johnson Publishing Company for "Flag Song" by Nancy Byrd Turner from *Wheels Westward* of the *Happy Hour Series*.

John A. Lomax for "Old Grumbler," recorded by Sid Jordan, and "The Lost Lamb," recorded by Emma Dusenbury.

Ailena Luce for "Little Girl, Where Are You Going?" "Morning and Night," "Ris, Ras," "The Shepherdess," "Singing," and "Welcome to the New Year" from *Canciones Populares*, published by Silver Burdett Company.

The Macmillan Company for permission to reprint the words of "Roadways" from *Poems* by John Masefield and "The Little Rose Tree" from *The Pointed People* by Rachel Field.

Flora L. McDowell for "Mothers Make a Home," adapted from the version found in *Songs of the Old Camp Ground* by L. L. McDowell, published by Edwards Brothers, Inc.

Mary Newcomb for "The Birds' Conversation," "Hey, Little Boy!" "A Little Bit of Anything," and additional verses of "Polly Wolly Doodle."

Novello & Co., Ltd. for "The Keeper" from *Folk Songs*, collected and arranged by Cecil J. Sharp, copyright, 1909.

Moira O'Neill and Wm. Blackwood & Sons, Ltd., for permission to use the words of "Sleep, Little Child" from *Songs and More Songs of the Glens of Antrim*.

For special services, grateful acknowledgment is made to the following:

Lillian L. Baldwin, Cleveland, Ohio, for constructive suggestions in the Listening Program.

Alice C. Cooper for assistance in the selection of poetry.

Edna W. Doll, Department of Physical Education, Clifford J. Scott High School, East Orange, New Jersey, for the organization and specific directions in rhythmic activities.

Charles and Ruth Seeger for research into American folk lore and folk song literature.

Bertha Donner, Esther Fenili, Kathrine Szal Millwood, Sylvia M. Pond, Maria Solano, and Hilya Tillander for English translations of foreign language texts.

(*Acknowledgments continued on p. 186*)

Copyright, 1945, by

SILVER BURDETT COMPANY

△

NEW MUSIC HORIZONS
Fourth Book

The Star-Spangled Banner

FRANCIS SCOTT KEY

The National Anthem

JOHN STAFFORD SMITH

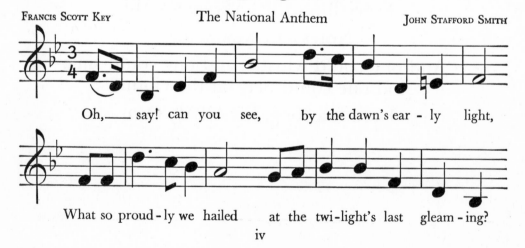

Oh,— say! can you see, by the dawn's ear-ly light,

What so proud-ly we hailed at the twi-light's last gleam-ing?

Whose broad stripes and bright stars, through the per - il - ous fight,

O'er the ram - parts we watched were so gal - lant - ly stream - ing?

And the rock - ets' red glare, the bombs burst - ing in air,

Gave proof through the night that our flag was still there.

Chorus

Oh, say, does that__ Star-Span-gled Ban - ner__ yet__ wave__

O'er the land_____ of the free and the home of the brave?

Pawpaw Patch

AMERICAN SINGING GAME

Dance Directions
Longways Formation

Third Verse

1. Where, oh where, is pret-ty lit-tle El - lie,

Where, oh where, is pret-ty lit-tle El - lie,

Where, oh where, is pret-ty lit-tle El - lie?

'Way down in the paw-paw patch.

2. Pickin' up pawpaws, puttin' 'em in the basket.
3. Here she comes and I'll go with her.
4. Swing a lady up and down, swing a lady home.

Four couples make a set. Any number of sets may join the dance. Partners stand in long-ways formation, facing each other.

Verse I. Head couple walk down and back between the lines, looking for Ellie.

Verse 2. Head couple down and back again, stooping to "pick up pawpaws and put 'em in the basket."

Verse 3. Head couple join hands, walk down center, cross over, and walk back outside oppos-ite line. Look at the diagram.

Verse 4. Head boy goes to girl number 2; they link right arms and swing around. He then does the same with girl number 3, and then with girl number 4. Head girl does the same down the line of boys. At last line of verse, head couple swing and take places at bot-tom of the lines. Second boy and girl now become the head couple and the dance goes on.

A pawpaw is the sweet, pulpy fruit of a small tree in the south.

Day Is Done

HAMBURG
Arranged by LOWELL MASON
from a GREGORIAN CHANT

VIRGINIA HARRISON

Day now is done, there's a star in the west,
When dark is gone and a new day be - gun,

Still is the land and the twi - light is deep,
Dawn in the sky and a light on the hill,

All things are read - y to turn to their rest,
We shall a - wake and be glad in the sun,

Fa - ther, Thy love is guard - ing our sleep.
Fa - ther, Thy love shall go with us still.

Drum Music for "Day Is Done"

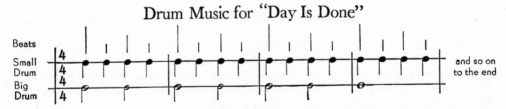

Beats

Small Drum

Big Drum

and so on to the end

4
4 The upper figure of the time signature tells us that there are four beats in a measure. The lower figure tells us that a quarter note equals one beat.

The notes of the song give the rhythm pattern which the voices sing.

You can march to this song, keeping step with the beats. At the same time you can clap the rhythm pattern of the notes.

4

A Fair Little Girl

LORD HOUGHTON

W. OTTO MIESSNER

A fair lit-tle girl sat un-der a tree,

Sew - ing as long as her eyes could see,

Then smoothed out her work and fold - ed it tight,

And said, "Dear work, good night, good night!"

Voice study. Sing "good night, good night" with long, smooth tones.   Sing it in higher and lower keys.

In A FAIR LITTLE GIRL the first and third phrases are alike, and the second and fourth phrases are different.   The phrase pattern can be called: A, B, A, C.

Noticing phrases that are alike and different will help you read music.   After you have read a phrase, you should be able to read it easily when it comes again.   You can also memorize music more easily if you notice which phrases are alike.

You can make up songs by building them of phrases that are alike and different.   That is the way composers make their music.   Notice the phrase patterns of the songs in this book and see how they are built.

Everybody enjoys listening to good songs and instrumental pieces.   Listening is a greater pleasure when you can hear the pattern of the phrases.

Look Up, There's the Flag!

NANCY BYRD TURNER

CHARLES WAKEFIELD CADMAN

1. Look_ up, there's the flag, How it shines o - ver - head,
2. With the wind in its folds And the earth at its foot,
3. It__ stands for the brave And the faith - ful and true,

With the sun_ on its col - ors, Its blue, white, and red!__
And the sky__ for its shel - ter, Hands up and sa - lute!__
For__ cour - age and hon - or; We'll stand for them too!__

5

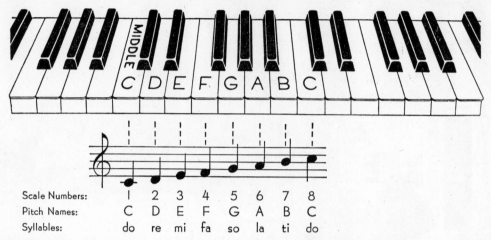

Scale Numbers:	1	2	3	4	5	6	7	8
Pitch Names:	C	D	E	F	G	A	B	C
Syllables:	do	re	mi	fa	so	la	ti	do

A tone is what you hear.   A note is what you see.   The scale in the key of C is shown above as it appears on the piano keyboard and on the staff. In this key, C is the home tone, called the key-note. Most songs sound best when they end on the key-note. THOSE EVENING BELLS is in the Key of C.   Look at the top of this page and find the notes and piano keys for the tones of THOSE EVENING BELLS. You then can play the song on the piano, on a set of bells, or on a C wind instrument.   You will be able to read the music of THOSE EVENING BELLS and can sing or play from the notes.

Those Evening Bells

THOMAS MOORE   OLD NURSERY TUNE

8	7	6	5	4	3	2	1	8	7	6	5	4	3	2	1
C	B	A	G	F	E	D	C	C	B	A	G	F	E	D	C
do	ti	la	so	fa	mi	re	do	do	ti	la	so	fa	mi	re	do

Those eve-ning bells! Those eve-ning bells! How man-y a tale their mu - sic tells

1	2	3	4	3	4	5	6	5	6	7	8	5	6	7	8
C	D	E	F	E	F	G	A	G	A	B	C	G	A	B	C
do	re	mi	fa	mi	fa	so	la	so	la	ti	do	so	la	ti	do

Of youth, and home, and that sweet time When last I heard their sooth-ing   chime.

Swinging

NETTIE ALBERT

FOLK SONG from MORAVIA

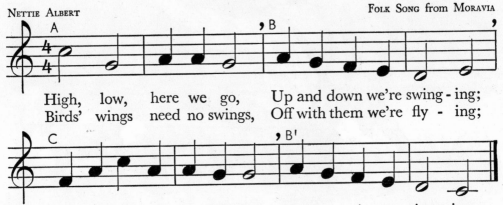

High, low, here we go, Up and down we're swing-ing;
Birds' wings need no swings, Off with them we're fly - ing;

Lots of fun out in the sun, Hap-py voic-es ring-ing.
Back to town we're slow-ing down, Now the old cat's dy - ing.

Gentleness

From THE MODERN MUSIC SERIES

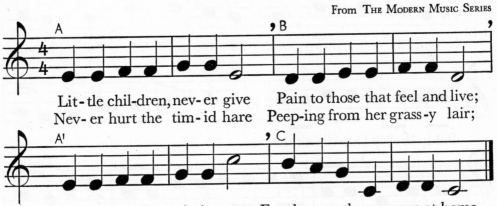

Lit-tle chil-dren, nev-er give Pain to those that feel and live;
Nev-er hurt the tim-id hare Peep-ing from her grass-y lair;

Let the gen-tle rob-in come For the crumbs you save at home.
Let her come and sport and play On the lawn at close of day.

Notice how the phrase patterns are marked for the songs on this page. Phrases which are nearly alike are shown this way: A, A¹, or B, B¹.
You can step the beats and clap the rhythm pattern of the notes.

Polly Wolly Doodle

TRADITIONAL

AMERICAN FOLK SONG

1. Oh, I went down South for to see my Sal, Sing-ing
Pol-ly Wol-ly Doo-dle all the day; My Sal, she is a
spunk-y gal, Sing-ing Pol-ly Wol-ly Doo-dle all the day. Fare thee

CHORUS

well, fare thee well, Fare thee well, my fair - y

fay,   For I'm goin' to Loui-si-an-a, for to

see my Su-sy-an-na, Sing-ing Pol-ly Wol-ly Doo-dle all the day.

2. Oh, my Sal, she is a maiden fair,
   With curly eyes and laughing hair.

3. Oh, a grasshopper sittin' on a railroad track,
   A-pickin' his teeth with a carpet tack.

4. Oh, I went to bed, but it wasn't no use,
   My feet stuck out for the chickens to roost.

5. Behind the barn, down on my knees,
   I thought I heard a chicken sneeze.

6. He sneezed so hard with the whooping cough,
   He sneezed his head and tail right off.

7. The raccoon's tail is very large
   An' the 'possum's tail is bare;
   The rabbit has no tail at all,
   But a little bit a-bunch of hair.

8. The June bug he has golden wings,
   The lightnin' bug has fame;
   The weevil has no wings at all
   But he gets there just the same.

You can add some verses of your own.

9

Marching Song of the Shepherds

Translated from the SLOVAK
by MARION BERGMAN

SLOVAK FOLK SONG

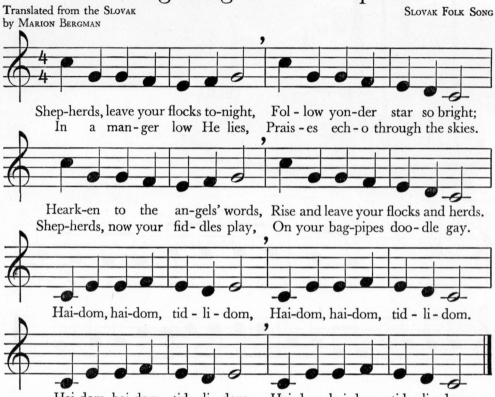

Shep-herds, leave your flocks to-night, Fol - low yon-der star so bright;
In a man-ger low He lies, Prais - es ech - o through the skies.

Heark-en to the an-gels' words, Rise and leave your flocks and herds.
Shep-herds, now your fid- dles play, On your bag-pipes doo- dle gay.

Hai-dom, hai-dom, tid - li - dom, Hai-dom, hai-dom, tid - li - dom.

Hai-dom, hai-dom, tid - li - dom, Hai-dom, hai-dom, tid - li - dom.

The people in Slovakia have an old folk tale. It is about the shepherds who brought their fiddles and bagpipes as they marched to greet the Christ-child. They have made it into a song. The chorus gives the sounds of their instruments.

You can march to this song. When marching, the left foot steps on the accented beats. The right foot steps on the unaccented beats.

There are many kinds of marches, with many different rhythm patterns. The drum music for MARCHING SONG OF THE SHEPHERDS is given below. Some pupils may play the part for the Big Drum and others may play the part for the Small Drum. Some can pretend they are playing a piano accompaniment; the left hand plays the lower part and the right hand plays the upper part.

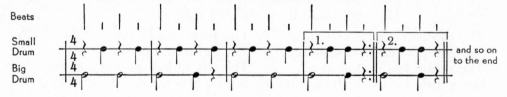

Beats

Small
Drum

Big
Drum

and so on
to the end

Time to Go to Sleep

From the FINNISH by
MARTHA DABNEY

CHILDREN'S SONG from FINLAND
by MIKAEL NYBERG

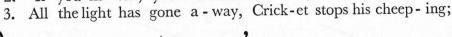

1. Light is fad - ing in the sky, Birds are home-ward wing-ing,
2. If you lis - ten, you will hear "Ta - ra, ta - ra, tid - dle;"
3. All the light has gone a - way, Crick-et stops his cheep-ing;

Shad-ows on the hill - top lie, Far a bell is ring - ing.
That's a crick-et some-where near Play-ing on his fid - dle.
This has been a   hap - py day, Now it's time for sleep-ing.

The River

From the GERMAN by
JANE ROLFE RANDOLPH

F. A. ALBRECHT

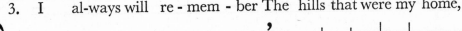

1. O tell me, pret - ty riv - er, How far your wa - ters come,
2. My home is in the moun-tains, Where I be-gan to be,
3. I al-ways will re - mem - ber The hills that were my home,

And if you're on a jour-ney now, Or are you go - ing home?
But now a wind-ing way I go To join the might-y sea.
But wa - ters find the sea at last, So to the sea I come.

THREE KINDS OF MARCHES

Faith of Our Fathers

Frederick W. Faber

Henry F. Hemy and J. G. Walton

1. Faith of our fa - thers, liv - ing still
2. Faith of our fa - thers, we will strive
3. Faith of our fa - thers, we will love

In spite of dun - geon, fire and sword;
To win all na - tions un - to thee;
Both friend and foe in all our strife,

Oh, how our hearts beat high with joy
And through the truth that comes from God
And preach thee, too, as love knows how,

When - e'er we hear that glo - rious word!
Man - kind will then in - deed be free.
By kind - ly words and vir - tuous life.

Refrain

Faith of our fa - thers, ho - ly faith,

We will be true to thee till death.

Go to Sleep, My Baby Child

Negro Lullaby from Virginia

Go   to sleep, my   ba - by child,   Go   to sleep, my lit-tle ba - by;

When   you wake___ you shall have   All   the pret-ty lit-tle hors - es,

Black and blue___ and   sor - rel, too, ___ All the pret-ty lit-tle hors-es.

Voice study.   Sing "Go to sleep, my little baby" (end of first line) in higher and lower keys.
Sing these tones with "ah," "oh," and "doo."

Evening Hymn

Reginald Heber   W. H. Monk

God, that mad - est earth and heav - en, Dark - ness and light;
And when morn a - gain shall call   us   To   run life's way,

Who the day for   toil hast giv - en, For   rest the night.
May we still, what-e'er be - fall us, Thy   will o - bey.

May Thine an-gel guards de-fend us, Slum-ber sweet Thy mer-cy send us;
From the pow'r of e - vil hide us, In the nar-row path-way guide us,

Ho-ly dreams and hopes at-tend us, This live-long night.
Nor Thy smile be e'er de-nied us The live-long day.

Time to Work

VIRGINIA HARRISON

REISSMANN

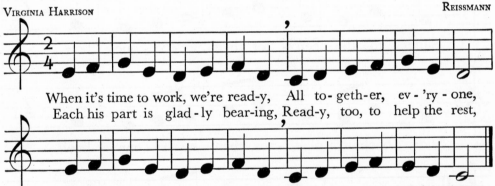

When it's time to work, we're read-y, All to-geth-er, ev - 'ry - one,
Each his part is glad-ly bear-ing, Read-y, too, to help the rest,

Will-ing, cheer-ful, strong and stead-y, That's the way our work is done.
Laugh-ing, try-ing, do-ing, shar-ing, That's the way we work the best!

Drum Music for "Time to Work"

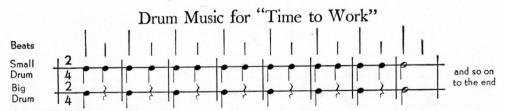

Beats
Small Drum
Big Drum

and so on to the end

2/4 The time signature tells us that there are two beats in a measure, and that a quarter note equals one beat.

You can step the beats and clap the note patterns.

Folk Dance

Danced in a circle. Partners face each other; hold hands crossed.

CYNTHIA STEWART

CZECH SINGING FOLK DANCE

Slide to the cen - ter, then ev - 'ry - one bow,

Slide back to plac - es, then ev - 'ry - one bow.

To the right, swing; To the left, swing;
To the left, swing; To the right, swing;

Cross hands and slide in a cir - cle, then bow.
Cross hands and slide in a cir - cle, then bow.

16

Mothers Make a Home

WHITE SPIRITUAL

RELIGIOUS FOLK SONG of the
TENNESSEE HILL COUNTRY

1. Moth-ers make a home, sweet home;
2. Fa-thers make a home, sweet home;
3. Beau-ti-ful home, sweet home;

Moth-ers make a home, sweet home;
Fa-thers make a home, sweet home;
Beau-ti-ful home, sweet home;

Moth-ers make a home, sweet home;
Fa-thers make a home, sweet home;
Beau-ti-ful home, sweet home;

How I love, I love my moth-er's
How I love, I love my fa-ther's
How I love, I love my home,

Beau-ti-ful home!
Beau-ti-ful home!
Beau-ti-ful home!

The Lost Lamb

TRADITIONAL

AMERICAN FOLK LULLABY

Baa   baa   black   sheep, Where'd you leave your lamb?   A-

way down yon-der in the val - ley,   The bees and the but-ter-flies A-

flit-ting round its eyes, And the poor lit-tle thing cried "Mam - my!"

My mam-my told me be-fore she went a-way To take good care of the

ba - by;   But I went out to play— and the ba-by ran a-way, And the

poor lit-tle thing cried "Mam - my!" The bees and the but-ter-flies A-

flit-ting round its eyes, And the poor lit-tle thing cried "Mam - my!"

Groundhog

TRADITIONAL

KENTUCKY MOUNTAIN SONG

1. Shoul-der up your gun and whis-tle up your dog,

Shoul-der up your gun and   whis-tle up your dog,

A - way   to the woods to   catch a ground-hog, ground - hog.

2. 'Long comes Mary with a great big pole,
   'Long comes Mary with a great big pole,
   To twist that groundhog outen his hole, groundhog.

3. Sharpen up your knife and take off his hide,
   Sharpen up your knife and take off his hide,
   We like groundhog both stewed and fried, groundhog.

Three Little Ships

Nancy Norwood

Hoagy Carmichael

Slowly

The great o-cean lin-ers sail brave-ly a-way;
Though great were the per-ils of breast-ing the wave,

They trav-el by night and by day._____
The heart of the lead-er was brave;_____

But brav-er than these were the ven-ture-some three,
His faith nev-er failed as they bat-tled the sea,

The *Pin-ta,* the *Ni-ña,* the *San-ta Ma-rie.*
The *Pin-ta,* the *Ni-ña,* the *San-ta Ma-rie.*

They had no en-gines to pull them through gales,
You o - cean lin-ers that jour-ney with pride,

They trav-eled by gath-er-ing wind in their sails.
Re - mem-ber who first crossed the o - cean so wide:

Co - lum-bus was proud as he gazed at the three,
Co - lum-bus the brave and his ven-ture-some three,

The *Pin - ta,* the *Ni - ña,* the *San - ta Ma - rie.*
The *Pin - ta,* the *Ni - ña,* the *San - ta Ma - rie.*

21

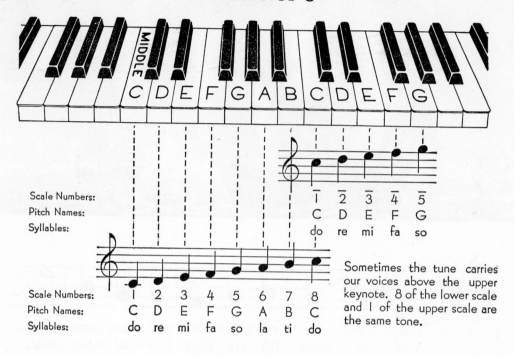

Scale Numbers: 1̄   2̄   3̄   4̄   5̄
Pitch Names: C   D   E   F   G
Syllables: do   re   mi   fa   so

Scale Numbers: 1   2   3   4   5   6   7   8
Pitch Names: C   D   E   F   G   A   B   C
Syllables: do   re   mi   fa   so   la   ti   do

Sometimes the tune carries our voices above the upper keynote. 8 of the lower scale and 1 of the upper scale are the same tone.

The Road

NANCY BYRD TURNER   FOLK SONG from YUGOSLAVIA

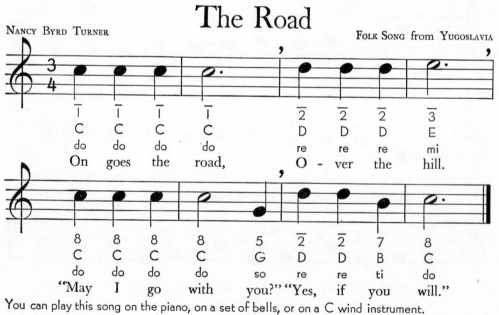

1̄	1̄	1̄	1̄	2̄	2̄	2̄	3̄
C	C	C	C	D	D	D	E
do	do	do	do	re	re	re	mi
On	goes	the	road,	O-	ver	the	hill.

8	8	8	8	5	2̄	2̄	7	8
C	C	C	C	G	D	D	B	C
do	do	do	do	so	re	re	ti	do
"May	I	go	with	you?"	"Yes,	if	you	will."

You can play this song on the piano, on a set of bells, or on a C wind instrument.

Puppet Show

VIRGINIA HARRISON   MORAVIAN FOLK TUNE

Pup - pet Show! Pup - pet Show! See the pup - pets play - ing;
Light - ly go, heel and toe, Ev - 'ry pull o - bey - ing.

Watch them jump, jerk and bump, Do - ing fun - ny things!
Would you prance, bob and dance, If I pulled your strings?

Voice study. Sing this lively tune using the syllables "ah" and "tra la la," etc.
Make your voices ringing and clear. Sing it in higher and lower keys.

Worship

SALISBURY COLLECTION   WÜRTTEMBERG CHORALE

1. Ho - ly, ho - ly, ho - ly Lord, Be Thy glo - rious name a - dored!
2. Though un - wor - thy, Lord, Thine ear Deign our hum - ble songs to hear;
3. Then with an - gel harps a - gain We will wake a no - ble strain;

Lord, Thy mer - cies nev - er fail; Hail, ce - les - tial good - ness, hail!
Pur - er songs we hope to bring, When a - round Thy throne we sing.
There in joy - ful songs of praise Our tri - um - phant voic - es raise.

The Animal Fair

AMERICAN HUMOROUS FOLK SONG

I went to the an-i-mal fair, —— The birds and the beasts were

there, —— The big ba-boon, by the light of the moon, Was

comb-ing his au - burn hair. —— You ought to have seen the

monk; —— He jumped on the el-e-phant's trunk; —— The

24

el - e - phant sneezed and fell on his knees, And

what be-came of the monk, the monk? I monk?____

Hallowe'en

KATE COX GODDARD

LILLIAN MOHR FOX

I cut a lit - tle pump-kin face, A mouth, a nose, and eyes;

I left it by a neigh-bor's door And laughed at their sur-prise.

I rang the bell and ran a-way, But then looked round to___ see

The fun - ny yel - low pump-kin face Just grin-ning back at me.

Butterflies

NANCY BYRD TURNER

ITALIAN FOLK SONG

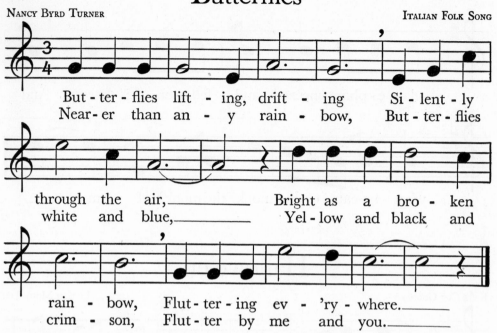

But - ter - flies lift - ing, drift - ing Si - lent - ly
Near - er than an - y rain - bow, But - ter - flies

through the air,_____ Bright as a bro - ken
white and blue,_____ Yel - low and black and

rain - bow, Flut - ter - ing ev - 'ry - where._____
crim - son, Flut - ter by me and you._____

Voice study. Sing the last phrase with the syllables "so, so, so, mi, re, do," in higher and lower keys. Sing it also with "ho, ho, ho," etc. This is a fine voice study!

John's Beautiful Horse

Translated from the SLOVAK
by AILEEN FISHER

SLOVAK FOLK SONG

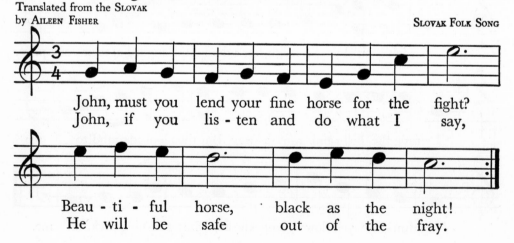

John, must you lend your fine horse for the fight?
John, if you lis - ten and do what I say,

Beau - ti - ful horse, black as the night!
He will be safe out of the fray.

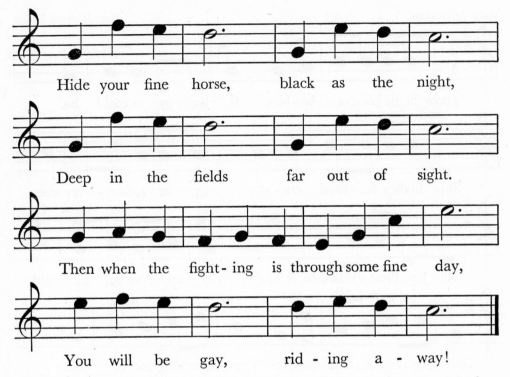

Hide your fine horse, black as the night,

Deep in the fields far out of sight.

Then when the fight- ing is through some fine day,

You will be gay, rid - ing a - way!

Waltz Walk: Walk three steps forward (one measure). The first step is on the whole foot, the second and third steps are on the toes. Continue same movement, beginning with the other foot.

You can waltz walk to these songs while clapping the note patterns.

Rhythm of the Waltz

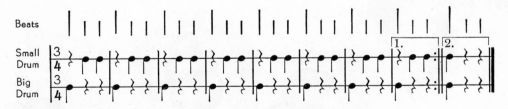

$\frac{3}{4}$ The time signature tells us that there are three beats in a measure and that a quarter note equals one beat.

Chestnut Babies

MABEL LIVINGSTONE

KATE WARNER LEROY

Three lit-tle chest-nut ba-bies, As hap-py as could be,

Slept in their fur-lined cra-dles, Up in a chest-nut tree;

Till Jack Frost shook them rough-ly, "Get up, get up," he said,

And then the chest-nut ba-bies Came tum-bling out of bed.

FAIRY TALES IN MUSIC

Theme: DANCE OF THE TOY FLUTES, from "THE NUTCRACKER" SUITE — TSCHAIKOWSKY

Theme: WALTZ, from "THE SLEEPING BEAUTY" — TSCHAIKOWSKY

WALTZ, ROSES FROM THE SOUTH — STRAUSS. See song on page 108.

Many of the songs in this book may be played on several kinds of simple flutes and on the recorder. These instruments are pleasing to play, and they also prepare the way for playing some of the instruments of the orchestra and the band. Some types of flutes are made to play in only a few keys. You can select songs in those keys, or you can play the melodies in the keys in which your flute can play.

Work Time and Sleep Time

CHILDREN'S SONG from FINLAND
by J. F. FRANCKE

ANNETTE WYNNE

Day-time is the time for light, Bet-ter work be-fore the night,
Day-time work is al-ways best; Best to keep the night for rest;

Bet-ter get your tasks all done And your play-ing in the sun.
Night was meant for sleep, no doubt, God then puts the sun's light out.

Reprinted with permission from FOR DAYS AND DAYS by Annette Wynne. Copyright 1919 by J. B. Lippincott Company.

Horses in the Field
(Čtyři koně ve dvoře)

From the original CZECH by
JANE ROLFE RANDOLPH

CZECH FOLK SONG

In waltz tempo

Three good hors - es in the field, Who will
John will come and find them soon, Champ - ing,
Čty - ři ko - ně ve dvo - ře, žád - nej

come to set them plow-ing there? Three good hors - es
stamp - ing, neigh - ing, nod-ding there; John will drive them
s ni - ma ne - vo - ne - vo - ře, čty - ři ko - ně

big and strong, Wait - ing, all, the mo-ment to go.
down the field; Three good hors - es, all in a row.
ve dvo - ře, žád - nej s ni - ma ne - vo - ře.

Flute Tunes from China

In China, the street peddlers attract attention by playing little tunes on their flutes. Their flutes are made of bamboo. Here are two typical Chinese peddlers' tunes.

Man with a Whistle

CHINESE FOLK TUNE

Blind Beggar with a Flute

CHINESE FOLK TUNE

The Pirate

Margaret B. Schwoerer

Charles Wakefield Cadman

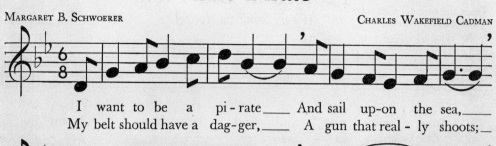

I want to be a pi-rate____ And sail up-on the sea,____
My belt should have a dag-ger,____ A gun that real-ly shoots;____

And ev-'ry kid in our whole block Would be a-fraid of me.____
A skull and cross-bones on my hat, And high swash-buck-ling boots.____

I want some big black whisk-ers,___ A scarf a-round my head,___
Like Cap-tain Kidd I'd swag-ger,___ And be as tough as he;___

With hard-tack on - ly for my food, And ship-deck for my bed.___
And I will be the bold - est man That ev - er sailed the sea.___

Prayer at Morning

Martha Dabney

Andreas Hammerschmidt (1658)
Harmonized by Bach

Lord, we lift our prayer to Thee, Now an-oth-er day has start-ed;
In this world that is our home, When we're work-ing, play-ing, sleep-ing,

Let us spend it lov-ing-ly, Make us kind and gen-tle-heart-ed;
When we go, and when we come, Still our lives are in Thy keep-ing;

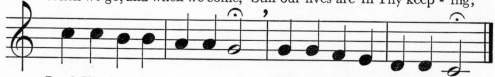

Lord, Thy love for-ev-er stays With us all our nights and days.
Lord, Thy love for-ev-er stays With us all our nights and days.

Come Out to Play

Virginia Harrison

Czech Folk Song

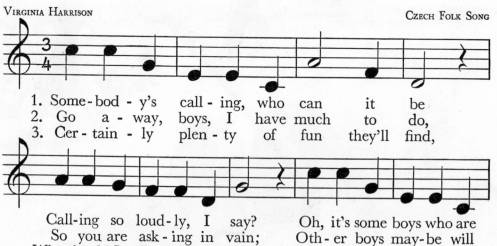

1. Some-bod-y's call-ing, who can it be
2. Go a-way, boys, I have much to do,
3. Cer-tain-ly plen-ty of fun they'll find,

Call-ing so loud-ly, I say? Oh, it's some boys who are
So you are ask-ing in vain; Oth-er boys may-be will
Why should I lin-ger at home? Boys, I be-lieve I will

ask - ing me   If I won't come out and play.
go with you.   No, they are call-ing a - gain!
change my mind,   Wait just a min-ute, I'll come!

Fooba Wooba John

AMERICAN FOLK SONG

Saw a flea kick a tree, Foo-ba woo-ba, foo-ba woo-ba,
Saw a louse chase a mouse, Foo-ba woo-ba, foo-ba woo-ba,

Saw a flea kick a tree, Foo - ba woo - ba John.
Saw a louse chase a mouse, Foo - ba woo - ba John.

Saw a flea kick a tree In the mid-dle of the sea;
Saw a louse chase a mouse From the kitch-en to the house;

Whoa, John, old John, Foo - ba woo - ba John.
Whoa, John, old John, Foo - ba woo - ba John.

You can add some verses of your own.

Sleep, Little Child

Moira O'Neill   Marshall Bartholomew

Sleep, lit-tle child, sleep soft - ly___ here,
Sleep, lit-tle child, nor fear the___ night,

An - gels of God are watch - ing___ near;
Af - ter the dark comes morn - ing___ light;

Thou shalt be safe, lay_down thy head,___
An - gels re - turn, their_home to see,___

With their white wings_a - bove_thee_ spread.
God look-eth down_and_ lov - eth___ thee.

The Squirrels' Thanksgiving

Frank H. Swett

Eleanor Smith

Up in the top of a wal - nut tree Squir-rels are hav-ing a ju - bi-lee,

Bright and gay, they frisk and play, Hold-ing their har - vest hol - i - day,

Show-ing their thanks in squir-rel pranks For gath-ered nuts they have stored a-way.

Waltzing

Adapted from the CREOLE by
ALICE WHITSON NORTON

CREOLE SONG from LOUISIANA

1.-2. Waltz on, waltz on, So dain - ty and bright,

Waltz on, waltz on, So grace-ful and light!

1. Now turn to the left, Now turn to the right,
2. Now float-ing a - way Like birds in their flight,

1.-2. Waltz on, waltz on, So dain - ty and bright,

Waltz on, waltz on, So grace-ful and light!

Waltz Step: Step forward right foot; step sideways left foot; close right foot to left (first measure). Repeat, beginning with left foot (second measure). Continue, stepping backward the next two measures.

The Brownie Dance

NANCY BYRD TURNER   MEXICAN FOLK TUNE

1. Twen-ty Brown-ie boys were twirl-ing
2. On they ca-pered, gay and spright-ly,
3. For-ty Brown-ies, wind-ing, weav-ing,

In the woods be-yond the mead-ow,
All at once, as they were pranc-ing,
Danced a-round the dell and through it.

They were glid-ing, wheel-ing, whirl-ing,
Ev-'ry shad-ow bowed po-lite-ly,
If you think I'm make-be-liev-ing

Each was danc-ing with his shad-ow.
Twen-ty Brown-ie girls were danc-ing.
Ask the owl who saw them do it!

39

This Is the Day the Child Was Born

JAMES BOYD   MARSHALL BARTHOLOMEW

1. This is the day the Child was born,

All free from blame, all free from blame,

Who bore the wound and wore the thorn

To save the sin - ful and for - lorn

40

Who speak His_ name, who speak_ His_ name.

2. On shepherds a new light shone down,
   That Christmastide, that Christmastide,
   New voices sang above the town,
   A song of cheer whose holy sound
   Hath never died, hath never died.

3. Therefore we sing of Thee today,
   Where'er we are, where'er we are,
   All humbly trusting that we may
   Be guided by Thee on our way
   As by a star, as by a star.

4. Then may we ponder, one by one,
   On every child, on every child,
   In every land beneath the sun,
   Whose life on earth, just now begun,
   Is undefiled, still undefiled.

5. And thereon take good hope anew
   From Thy bright birth, from Thy bright birth,
   That those who seek Thy will to do
   May to all men and children, too,
   Bring peace on earth, bring peace on earth.

41

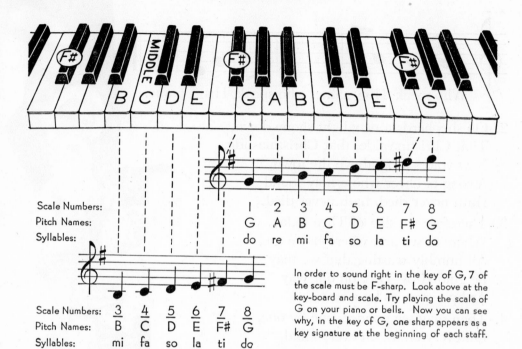

Scale Numbers: 1   2   3   4   5   6   7   8

Pitch Names: G A B C D E F# G

Syllables: do re mi fa so la ti do

Scale Numbers: 3 4 5 6 7 8

Pitch Names: B C D E F# G

Syllables: mi fa so la ti do

In order to sound right in the key of G, 7 of the scale must be F-sharp. Look above at the key-board and scale. Try playing the scale of G on your piano or bells. Now you can see why, in the key of G, one sharp appears as a key signature at the beginning of each staff.

Morning

CYNTHIA STEWART

From HAYDN

3 3 2 2 1 5 5 5 6 6 2
B B A A G D D D E E A
mi mi re re do so so so la la re
When the light of morn - ing Gilds the east-ern sky,

4 4 3 3 2 6 1 1 2 2 1
C C B B A E G G A A G
fa fa mi mi re la do do re re do
Let us join in sing - ing Praise to God on high.

Lullaby
(*Arrullo*)

From the SPANISH by
MARTHA DABNEY

SPANISH AMERICAN FOLK SONG

Lul - la - by, my ba - by, Moth-er's ver - y near;
Duér - me - te mi ni - ño, Duér - me - te mi sol;

To her heart she'll fold you, Go to sleep, my dear.
Duér - me - te pe - da - zo De mi co - ra - zón.

The Church Bells

MARIE F. HALL

MARIE F. HALL

Ding dong! Hear the bells ring - ing from the stee - ple;

"Come to church," they seem to say, "all you good peo - ple."

Voice study. Sing all of this song with "dong, dong." Make your voices sound like clear bells. Then sing it with words and make your tones just as bell-like as before. Sing it in higher and lower keys.

We Three Kings of Orient Are

John Henry Hopkins

John Henry Hopkins

1. We three kings of O-ri-ent are, Bear-ing gifts we trav-erse a - far
2. Born a King on Beth-le-hem plain, Gold I bring to crown Him a-gain,
3. Frank-in-cense to of-fer have I, In-cense owns a De - i - ty nigh;

Field and foun-tain, moor and moun-tain, Fol-low-ing yon-der star.
King for - ev - er, ceas-ing nev - er, O-ver us all to reign.
Prayer and prais-ing, all men rais - ing, Wor-ship Him, God on high.

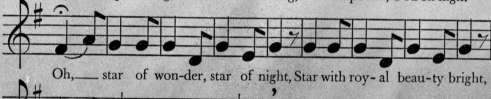

Oh,___ star of won-der, star of night, Star with roy-al beau-ty bright,

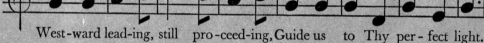
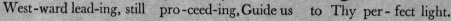

West-ward lead-ing, still pro-ceed-ing, Guide us to Thy per - fect light.

4. Myrrh is mine, its bitter perfume
   Breathes a life of gathering gloom;
   Sorrowing, sighing, bleeding, dying,
   Sealed in the stone-cold tomb.

5. Glorious now behold Him arise,
   King and God and Sacrifice;
   Heav'n sings Alleluia,
   Alleluia the earth replies.

Old Hundred

PSALM 100

LOUIS BOURGEOIS (1551)

1. Ye   na - tions round the   earth, re - joice
2. The Lord   is   God; 'tis   He   a - lone
3. En - ter His gates with songs of   joy,
4. The Lord   is   good, the Lord   is   kind;

Be - fore   the Lord your Sov-'reign King,
Doth   life and breath and   be - ing give;
With   prais - es   to   His courts re - pair,
Great   is   His grace, His mer - cy sure;

Serve   Him with cheer - ful   heart and voice,
We   are   His work, and   not   our   own,
And   make   it   your di - vine em - ploy
And   the whole race of   man   shall find

With   all your tongues His glo - ry sing.
The   sheep that on   His pas - tures live.
To   pay your thanks and hon - ors there.
His   truth from age   to   age   en - dure.

45

Playing the Piano

GEORGE L. WRIGHT

Fingering

I can play the pi - an - o, you see,____

All my songs are so love - ly to me,____

When I fin - ger the keys With the great-est of ease

It is sim - ple as sim - ple can be.____

Fingers of the Right Hand

Every one who enjoys music should be able to play the piano, even if only well enough to play simple melodies. Playing the piano is a great help in learning to read music. It is also an excellent background for learning to play any other musical instrument.

When you are learning to play the piano you should try to use the proper fingers.

The fingering for PLAYING THE PIANO is given above the notes. Any good piano course will help you to learn to play with correct fingering.

The Milkman

Adapted from CHRISTOPHER MORLEY*

A. BRANDT

Ear - ly in the morn - ing Dawn is on the roofs,
Hear the bot - tles clink - ing; Then he drives a - way;

Hear his wheels come roll - ing, Hear his hor - se's hoofs.
Yawn in bed, turn o - ver, Start an - oth - er day.

* From *Songs For a Little House*, copyright, 1917, by Christopher Morley.
Published by J. B. Lippincott Company.

Singing

(*Los niños en España cantan*)

From the SPANISH by
JANE ROLFE RANDOLPH

SPANISH AMERICAN FOLK SONG

The chil-dren sing in sun-ny Spain, They sing in old Pe - ru,
Their tunes are full of mer-ry words; It is a hap-py thing
Los ni - ños en Es - pa - ña can - tan can - tan en Pe - rú

Their lit - tle songs with quick re-frain, The way the rob - ins do.
To watch the chil-dren and the birds And hear the songs they sing!
Los pa - ja - ri - tos can - tan de a - le - grí - a y sa - lud.

Thanksgiving Day Song

NANCY BYRD TURNER

KAY KELLOGG

Thanks-giv-ing Day has come;_Light the fire,__ red and cheer-y,
It's chill No-vem-ber weath-er, But the fire-light's on the wall.__

Let's be glad of heart, and mer-ry, Thank-ing God for home.__
Home, dear home, is best of all;__ Let's thank God to-geth-er.__

Come, Ye Thankful People, Come

HENRY ALFORD

GEORGE J. ELVEY

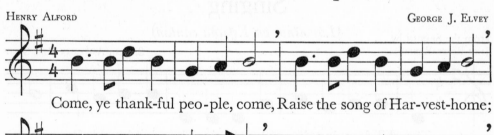

Come, ye thank-ful peo-ple, come, Raise the song of Har-vest-home;

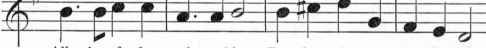

All is safe-ly gath-ered in, Ere the win-ter storms be-gin;

God, our Mak-er, doth pro-vide For our wants to be sup-plied;

Come to God's own tem-ple, come, Raise the song of Har-vest-home.

Christmas Chorale

First stanza: Translated by Rev. John Troutbeck
Second stanza: Translated by Catherine Winkworth

Harmonized by
Johann Sebastian Bach

With - in yon low - ly man - ger lies
Good news from heav'n the an - gels bring,

The Lord who reigns a - bove the skies;
Glad ti - dings to__ the__ earth they sing.

With - in the stall where beasts have fed
To us this day__ a Child__ is giv'n,

The Vir - gin - born doth__ lay__ His head.
To crown us with the__ joy__ of heav'n.

Voice study. Sing the last line of this lovely chorale with "ding, dong," like a Christmas chime. Sing it in several higher keys. Sing it with the words and make your voices just as beautiful as you can.

Drovers' Song

OLD AMERICAN SINGING GAME

1. Hog dro-vers, hog dro-vers, hog dro-vers we are,
2. I have but one daugh-ter, she sits by my side,
3. Care nought for your daugh-ter, much less for your-self,
4. I have but one daugh-ter, she sits by my knee,

A - court-ing your daugh-ter so neat and so fair,
And none of you dro-vers can get her for bride;
We'll trav-el on fur-ther and seek bet-ter wealth;
And Mis-ter can get her from me

Can we get lodg - ing here, oh here,
You can't have lodg - ing here, oh here,
We don't want lodg - ing here, oh here,
By bring-ing a pret-tier one here, oh here,

Can we get lodg - ing here?
You can't have lodg - ing here.
We don't want lodg - ing here.
By bring-ing a pret-tier one here.

A boy and girl are the father and daughter. They sit in the middle of the room. The other girls sit around the walls. Stanza 1. The hog drovers (boys) march around the father and daughter. Stanza 2. They stop while the father sings. Stanza 3. The hog drovers march around again. Stanza 4. They stop as the father sings stanza 4. He names one of the boys (line 2), who goes to a girl, bows to her, takes her hand, then dances (waltz step) back, and exchanges her for the daughter, who becomes his partner. The game starts over and continues until all the girls and boys have partners.

Little Star

ELLIOTT'S COLLECTION

NORMAL MUSIC COURSE

1. Lit - tle star____ that shines so bright,____
2. Lit - tle star,____ O tell me, pray,____
3. Lit - tle child,____ at you I peep,____
4. For I've man - y friends on high,____

Come and peep____ at me____ to - night,
Where you hide____ your - self____ all day;
While you lie____ so fast____ a - sleep;
Liv - ing with____ me in____ the sky;

For I of - ten watch for you
Have you got____ a home, like me,
But when morn____ be - gins to break,
And a lov - ing Fa - ther, too,

In the pret - ty sky so blue.
And a fa - ther kind to see?
I my home - ward jour - ney take.
Who com - mands____ what I've to do.

Sometimes one word or one syllable of a word is sung to two notes. These notes are grouped by a curved line, called a *slur*. Find all the slurs in LITTLE STAR.

TWO MASTER COMPOSERS

Theme: PRELUDE IN A-MAJOR — CHOPIN

Theme: AIR, from SUITE No. 3 IN D — BACH
Arranged for violin G-string by AUGUST WILHELMJ

O Little Town of Bethlehem

Phillips Brooks

L. H. Redner

1. O lit - tle town of Beth - le - hem! How still we see thee lie;
2. For Christ is born of Mar - y, And, gath - ered all a - bove,
3. How si - lent - ly, how si - lent - ly The won - drous gift is giv'n;
4. O ho - ly Child of Beth - le - hem! De - scend to us, we pray;

A - bove thy deep and dream - less sleep The si - lent stars go by.
While mor - tals sleep the an - gels keep Their watch of won - d'ring love.
So God im - parts to hu - man hearts The bless - ings of His Heav'n.
Cast out our sin and en - ter in, Be born in us to - day!

Yet in thy dark streets shin - eth The ev - er - last - ing Light;
O morn - ing stars, to - geth - er Pro - claim the ho - ly birth!
No ear may hear His com - ing, But in this world of sin,
We hear the Christ - mas an - gels The great, glad ti - dings tell;

The hopes and fears of all the years Are met in thee to - night.
And prais - es sing to God the King, And peace to men on earth.
Where meek souls will re - ceive Him still, The dear Christ en - ters in.
O come to us, a - bide with us, Our Lord Im - man - u - el!

Old Lochaber Lullaby

ANCIENT SCOTTISH FOLK SONG

Lul - la - by, rock - a - by, dear lit - tle ba by,

Shall we go sail - ing to Sleep - y - land, may - be?

O - ver the Snug-gle-down O - cean and un - der,

Shall we be ver - y long go - ing, I won - der?

You can step this song on tiptoe while lightly clapping the note patterns.

Welcome to the New Year

MARTHA DABNEY

LATIN AMERICAN FOLK TUNE

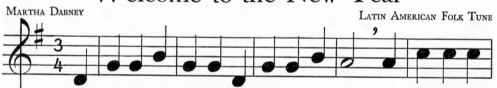

The New Year is com-ing, Sing east and sing west, The New Year is
The New Year is com-ing, Sing far and sing near, We're watch-ing and

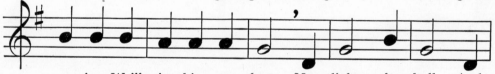

com-ing, We'll give him our best. Now light the hall And
wait-ing To give him good cheer. Fling wide the gate, He

win - dows all, With ev - 'ry- one read - y To wel-come our guest.
will not wait, Now wel-come, and wel-come, And wel-come, New Year!

Prayer
(*Modlitwa dziecka*)

Adapted from the original POLISH by
JANE ROLFE RANDOLPH

POLISH FOLK SONG

Fa - ther in Heav - en, may Thy love guide us,
Let Thy dear bless - ings fall on our home, Lord,
Do Cie - bie, Bo - że, rącz - ki pod - no - szę,

All through the day - light mov - ing be - side us,
Un - der our roof - tree may Thy love come, Lord.
O - zdro - wie Ta - ty i Ma - my pro - szę.

And when the night falls, while we are sleep - ing,
Work - ing or play - ing, wak - ing or sleep - ing,
I pro - szę tak - że, niech mnie od złe - go

Hold us, we pray Thee, safe in Thy keep - ing!
Oh, let our lives be safe in Thy keep - ing!
Na każ - dym kro - ku A nioł - ki strze - żą!

The Christmas Tree

From the original NORWEGIAN by
CYNTHIA STEWART

EDVARD HAGERUP GRIEG

Oh, hap - py, glis-ten-ing Christ-mas tree, We gath-er round you and
A-round the tree on the floor be-low Are Christ-mas pres-ents all
Du grøn - ne, glit-ren-de tre, god-dag, Vel-kom-men du som vi

sing with glee; Your lights are gleam-ing so bright and gay, You're
row on row, And stock-ings hang on the branch-es, too, All
ser saa gjer-ne Med ju - le-lys og med nor - ske flagg Og

decked in span-gles and fine__ ar - ray.__ A star that's shin-ing so
full of good-ies for me__ and you.__ The star that shines from the
høyt i top-pen den blan - ke stjer-ne, Ja den skal skin - ne, for

high a - bove Tells of God's_____ great love._____
bough a - bove Tells of God's_____ great love._____
den skal min - ne Oss om_____ vaar Gud._____

English Nursery Rhyme

1. I saw three ships come sail - ing by,
2. And what d'you think was in them then,
3. Three pret - ty girls were in them then,

Sail - ing by, sail - ing by,
In — them then, in — them then,
In — them then, in — them then

I saw three ships come sail - ing by,
And what d'you think was in them then,
Three pret - ty girls were in them then,

On Cris-si-mas Day in the morn - ing.
On Cris-si-mas Day in the morn - ing?
On Cris-si-mas Day in the morn - ing.

4. And one could whistle, and one could sing,
And one could play on the violin;
Such joy there was at my wedding,
On Crissimas Day in the morning.

You can skip to this song while
clapping the Note Patterns.

Old Grumbler

OLD AMERICAN SINGING GAME

1. Old Grum-bler is dead and laid un-der the ground,

Un-der the ground, un-der the ground;

Old Grum-bler is dead and laid un-der the ground,

'Way high up.

2. His saddle and bridle lay under the shade.
3. There stood an old apple tree over his head.
4. The apples were ripe and ready to drop.
5. There came an old lady a-picking them up.
6. Old Grumbler he rose and he gave her a knock.
7. That made the old lady go hippety-hop.
8. She hippety-hopped to Strawberry Hill.
9. And there she sat down and made her will.
10. If you want any more, you'll sing it yourself.

The action of the game is explained in verses 1, 3, 4, 5, and 6.
Verse 1: Form a circle. One child, Old Grumbler, lies in the center of the circle.
Verses 3 and 4: Another child stands at Grumbler's head and acts the part of the Tree.
Verse 5: The Old Lady goes into the ring and picks up apples.
Verses 6 - 10: Grumbler jumps up and tries to tag the Old Lady. She runs outside the circle.
  The Tree tries to get in Grumbler's way but must not hold him. If the Old Lady can get
  outside the ring and back into it again before Grumbler tags her, she is safe. Grumbler must
  try it all over again with another Old Lady and another Tree. If the Old Lady is tagged, she
  becomes the next Grumbler.

The First Nowell

TRADITIONAL

The Storm King

ANNIE WILLIS McCULLOUGH

EDWARD BAILEY BIRGE

The   Storm King's out this win-ter night
To - mor - row   all the world will lie

With   all_____ his mer - ry   men,
One   shin - ing stretch of   snow,

With   bold North Wind so   keen and bright,
Be - neath a   blue and   cloud - less sky.

60

And gay Jack Frost in drap - ings white,
"Hur - rah!" the boys and girls will cry

And snow imps howl-ing their de - light
And down the hills the sleds will fly,

That win - ter's__ come__ a - gain.
Then up more__ slow - ly go.

61

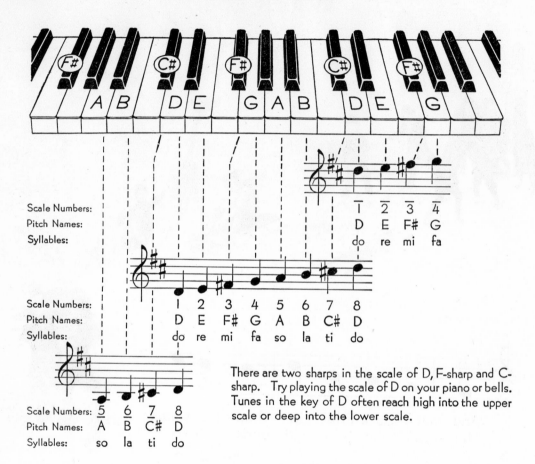

Scale Numbers:	1	2	3	4
Pitch Names:	D	E	F#	G
Syllables:	do	re	mi	fa

Scale Numbers:	1	2	3	4	5	6	7	8
Pitch Names:	D	E	F#	G	A	B	C#	D
Syllables:	do	re	mi	fa	so	la	ti	do

Scale Numbers:	5	6	7	8
Pitch Names:	A	B	C#	D
Syllables:	so	la	ti	do

There are two sharps in the scale of D, F-sharp and C-sharp. Try playing the scale of D on your piano or bells. Tunes in the key of D often reach high into the upper scale or deep into the lower scale.

The Storm
(Two-part Round)

W. A. WILLIAMS

1	1	3	1	3	1	5	5	5	5	5	5	5	5	8
D	D	F#	D	F#	D	A	A	A	A	A	A	A	A	D
do	do	mi	do	mi	do	so	so	so	so	so	so	so	so	do

Flash! Flash! Drip, drop, drip, drop! Pat-ter, pat-ter, pat-ter, pat-ter, Pour!

Winter Song

E. LOUISE LIDDELL

MODERN MUSIC SERIES

1. Sing a song of snow - flakes Fly-ing in the air;
2. Sing of feath-'ry snow - banks, Earth in daz-zling white;
3. Sing of mer - ry maid - ens, Sing of blithe-some boys,

Sing a song of sleigh bells Tin-kling ev - 'ry-where.
Sing of gleam-ing ice fields Spar-kling in the light.
Skat-ing, slid - ing, coast - ing, Full of fun and noise.

The Little Elf

JOHN KENDRICK BANGS

HÄRTER

I met a lit - tle Elf-man once, Down where the lil - ies
He slight-ly frowned, and with his eye He looked me through and

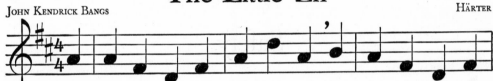

blow, I asked him why he was so small And
through. "I'm quite as big for me," said he, "As

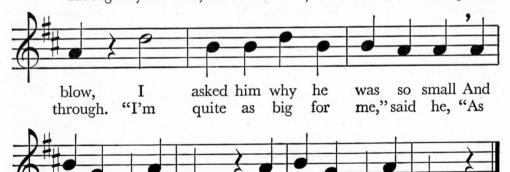

why he did not grow, And why he did not grow.
you are big for you, As you are big for you."

Pine Tree Song

MARJORIE BARROWS

NORWEGIAN FOLK SONG

1. Lit-tle pines up - on the hill, Sleep-ing in the moon-light still,
2. Ba-by moons of gold and red Cud-dle close be - side my head;
3. While my arms for girls and boys Blos-som with a hun-dred toys,

Are you dream-ing now of me, Bloomed in-to a Christ-mas tree?
In my tan-gled leaves a string, Fair-y stars are glim-mer-ing.
Lit-tle pines, it's fun to live As a Christ-mas tree, and give!

Safety

NADINE BENSLEY KEYES

NADINE BENSLEY KEYES

Be - side our house there is a street I have to cross each day,

The cars whiz past so ver-y fast, I al-ways wait un-til they've passed;

I look to right and look to left, Then safe-ly go my way.

Flag Song

NANCY BYRD TURNER

GEOFFREY O'HARA

Send it up to the tip of the staff, Flag of our land, no-ble and fair,

Bright in the sun and light in the wind, Brave on the air.

Ban-ner of free-dom, bright as the dawn; Off with the hat, up with the hand,

Pledg-ing our lives to bear it on, Flag of our land!

Snowflakes

Virginia Harrison

Czech Folk Song

White snow, light snow, White-ly, light-ly come, snow,

Cov-er for-est, field, and town, Shift-ing, sift-ing, drift-ing down.

Eighth notes may be printed in two ways. They may be joined by a crossbeam (♩♩) or each eighth note may have its own flag (♪ ♪). SNOWFLAKES is printed in both ways on this page. When eighth notes are joined by crossbeams, you can easily see the note groups. Now that you are using the Fourth Book, you will be able to see the note groups without this help.

You can step to the beats of this song while clapping the note patterns.

Snowflakes

Virginia Harrison

Czech Folk Song

White snow, light snow, White-ly, light-ly come, snow,

Cov-er for-est, field, and town, Shift-ing, sift-ing, drift-ing down.

A Quarter Note (♩) tells us to sing a tone one beat long.

A Half Note (♩) tells us to sing a tone two beats long.

Eighth Notes (♫) tell us to sing two tones while making one beat. Eighth rest (♲).
See p. 151.

What a Difference

MARION PHILLIPS

CZECH FOLK SONG

Ear - ly ev - 'ry morn - ing   Dad-dy comes to wake   me,
But at night it's dif - f'rent, Don't want to get   in   it;

Guess I'd nev - er leave my bed   If he did not make   me.
Beg to wait a   lit - tle while, Play an-oth-er min - ute.

How Grows the Bulb

JULIA W. BINGHAM

FOLK SONG from ITALY

1. Dry   lit - tle bulb bur-ied deep   in our gar - den,
2. Stiff lit - tle leaves soon will show   in our gar - den,
3. Gay   yel - low bud bloom-ing bright   in our gar - den,

Can   it   be   true   that you real - ly will grow
Heart of   the   bulb that we bur - ied last fall,
Tell - ing us   tru - ly when spring - time is here;

Un - der   the   snow,   Cold   win - ter snow?
Grow - ing so   tall,   Slen - der and tall.
Yes,   it   is   here,   Spring - time is here.

You can step to the beats of these songs while clapping the note patterns.

MEXICO AND ARABIA IN MUSIC

Theme: LA GOLONDRINA (THE SWALLOW)—SERRADELL

Moderato

Theme: ANITRA'S DANCE, from "PEER GYNT" SUITE—GRIEG

Tempo di Mazurka

68

The Potter's Wheel

Created by Guasti School
Mexican Children, Grades 4-5-6
San Bernardino County, California*

A-round and a-round—the pot-ter's wheel goes,
The bend-ing old pot-ter is wrin-kled and gray,

Turned by the pot - ter's strong brown toes,—
Work-ing and sing-ing, he's hap-py all day; The

Shap-ing the se-crets that he a-lone knows,
wheel whirls a-round and the pot-ter is gay,

Whirl-ing and whirl-ing, a-round the wheel goes.
Shap-ing his bowls with the soft yel-low clay.

Here is a song which was made up by school children, some of them in the Fourth Grade.
They made up both the words and the tune. Mrs. Spurgin helped write it. Mrs. Spurgin's
pupils have made up a number of songs. It was great fun. Wouldn't you like to make up
some songs of your own?

* Ernestine C. Spurgin, Supervisor of Music Education

69

My Lambs and My Sheep

Form: A, A, B, A
Translated from the CZECH by
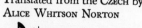
ALICE WHITSON NORTON

CZECH SINGING DANCE

I will tend my lambs and I will tend my sheep,
So with sweet, lov-ing care I will guard my flock

In their wool-ly coats, gray, black, and white;
Like a moth-er bird guards her wee nest;

When I call sweet-y, sweet-y, sweet, They an-swer bleat-y, bleat-y, bleat;
When I call sheep-y, sheep-y, sheep, They an-swer sleep-y, sleep-y, sleep;

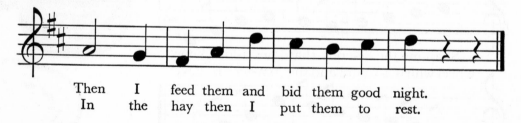

Then I feed them and bid them good night.
In the hay then I put them to rest.

The phrase pattern of MY LAMBS AND MY SHEEP is A, A, B, A. See if you can find other
A, A, B, A songs in this book. You may find some that have the A phrase changed a bit.
Phrases which are nearly alike are shown this way: A, A'.
You can Waltz Walk (see page 27) while clapping the note patterns.

Here is a poem to which you can make up your own A, A, B, A tune.   To help you, we will give
you the first phrase.   You will have to make up your own B phrase.   Then your teacher can
help you write the whole song.

> The sun goes down in clouds of red,
> The little sparrow hides its head,
> Now darkness comes to fields and homes,
> And ev'rything must go to bed.
>
> *Edith Lanham Bokeloh*

The   sun   goes   down   in   clouds   of   red,

Here is another poem to which you can make up an A, A, B, A tune.   This time you can make
up your own A phrase and also your own B phrase.   Then your teacher can help you write
the whole song.

> Merrily, merrily, cheerily, chee,
> Robin is happy as happy can be;
> All the long day he's chirping away,
> Flying and hopping and singing to me.
>
> *Ruth Stephens Porter*

Here is a poem for which it would be better to use a different phrase pattern.   Can you decide what the phrase pattern should be, and then write the tune?

> Twenty froggies went to school
> Down beside a rushy pool;
> Twenty little coats of green,
> Twenty vests all white and clean.
>
> *George Cooper*

What phrase pattern would you plan for this poem?

> The pine tree stands so still and proud,
> You never hear one talk out loud,
> But after dusk, if you will hark,
> You'll hear a whisper in the dark.
>
> *Eleanor Alletta Chaffee*

Now try making up your own poem as well as your own tune.   What would you like your poem
to tell about?

Wild Duck Feathers Falling
(*En roulant ma boule*)

Translated by
NANCY BYRD TURNER

FRENCH-CANADIAN FOLK SONG

Roll - ing, roll - ing, roll-ing a-long,
En   rou-lant ma bou - le rou-lant,

See   my ball a - roll - ing.   roll - ing.
En   rou-lant ma bou - le.   bou - le.

1. Three ducks are swim-ming on a pond, See my ball   a - roll-ing,
1. Der - rièr' chez nous y a - t'un - é-tang, En rou-lant ma bou - le,

72

They swim a-round, a-round, a-round,
Trois beaux ca-nards s'en vort bai-gnant,

D.C.

1.   2.

A-roll-ing, roll-ing, roll-ing a-long.   roll-ing a-long.
Rou-li, rou-lant, ma bou-le rou-lant.   bou-le rou-lant.

2. They swim around, then up they go,
   See my ball a-rolling, (*Repeat two lines.*)
   Their feathers fill the air like snow,
   A-rolling, rolling, rolling along. (*Repeat.*)

3. Those snowy feathers, soft and light,
   I'll catch to make a pillow white.

4. I'll sleep upon that pillow new
   And dream of ducks the whole night through!

2. *Trois beaux canards s'en vont baignant,*
   En roulant ma boule,
   Le fils du roi s'en va chassant,
   Rouli, roulant, ma boule roulant.

3. *Toutes ses plum's s'en vont au vent,*
   Trois dam's s'en vont les ramassant.

4. *Trois dam's s'en vont les ramassant,*
   C'est pour en faire un lit de camp.

PLAYING THE VIOLIN

There are many kinds of stringed instruments. You will think at once of guitars and banjos. Can you name any others? Some are plucked and some are played with a bow. "Fiddle" is the old name for stringed instruments played with a bow. The violin is the one we know best. It is played with a bow strung with hair from the tail of a horse.

A violin is played by drawing the bow with the right hand across one or more of the four strings. The four fingers of the left hand press the strings down on the fingerboard to make higher and lower tones. Sometimes another kind of sound is made by plucking the strings with the fingers. This is called *pizzicato*.

Many boys and girls learn to play the violin. Your own school orchestra must have a number of violin players. Perhaps you would like to join them.

TUNING THE VIOLIN

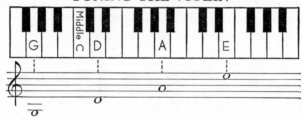

Someone who plays the violin can play these themes for you.

THEME
from the Ninth Symphony

LUDWIG VAN BEETHOVEN

Violin · *Andante*

FELIX BOROWSKI

Bright Morava

Translated from the CZECH by
JANE ROLFE RANDOLPH

FOLK SONG from MORAVIA

Past the fields of rye, Bright be-neath the sky,
Ver-y soft and clear Is the song we hear

Qui-et-ly our riv-er flows, Slow-ly on Mo-ra-va goes,
As the rip-pling riv-er comes Past our mead-ows and our homes,

Bright-ly glid-ing by.
Wind-ing far and near, Gay Mo-ra-va flows, Sing-ing as it goes.

Someone might play the violin with you while you sing this song.

My Dark Desert Maid

(*Asmar-i'l-Loun*)

Paraphrased from the ARABIC   FOLK SONG from NORTH AFRICA

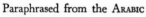

Dark eyes and_ jet black hair, My_ des-ert maid be - yond com-pare;

In the deep o - a - sis_ cool, She_ lin-gers by_ the_ lim - pid_ pool.

But when fades the sun-shine bright She sings and danc-es____with_ de - light.

Tin-kling bells and cym-bals cling To help Zu - lei - ka_ dance and_ sing.

Morning and Night

JEAN BASSETT   SPANISH AMERICAN FOLK TUNE

Dawn o-ver hill-tops wak - ing, High o-ver hill-tops wak - ing,
Slow-ly the sun is sink - ing, Slow o-ver mead-ows sink - ing;

Now is the morn-ing break-ing, Flood-ing the world with light.
Now all the stars come wink-ing, Bring-ing the qui-et night.

Winning the Race

JULIA W. BINGHAM   CZECH FOLK SONG

At a sign you take your place, All a-lert to   run the race;
E-ven if your legs are long, E-ven if your heart is strong,

But you will not   win   If you don't be - gin.
On-ly if you   run   Can the race be won.

Little Heidi

Anne Matheson

Anne Matheson

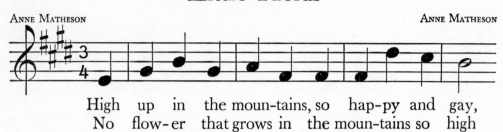

High   up   in   the moun-tains, so   hap-py   and   gay,
No   flow-er   that grows in   the moun-tains so   high

Dwells dear lit - tle   Hei - di, who sings all   the   day.
Is   fair - er   than Hei - di,   so   win-some and   shy.

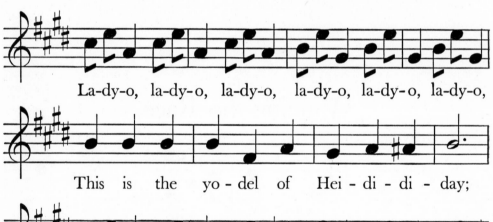

La-dy-o,   la-dy-o,   la-dy-o,   la-dy-o,   la-dy-o,   la-dy-o,

This   is   the   yo - del   of   Hei - di - di - day;

La-dy-o,   la-dy-o,   la-dy-o,   la-dy-o,   la-dy-o,   la-dy-o,

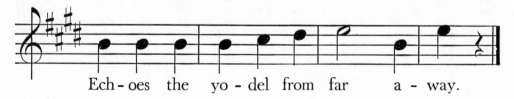

Ech - oes   the   yo - del from   far   a - way.

Jingle Bells

J. Pierpont   J. Pierpont

Dash-ing through the snow   In a   one-horse o - pen sleigh,

O'er the fields we go   Laugh-ing all the way; __ Bells on Bob-tail ring,

Mak- ing spir - its bright, What fun   it   is   to ride and sing A

Chorus

sleigh-ing song to-night!   Jin-gle bells, jin-gle bells, Jin-gle all the way!

Oh! what fun   it is   to ride In a one-horse o - pen sleigh! __

Jin - gle bells,   jin - gle bells,   Jin - gle   all   the way!

Oh! what fun   it   is   to ride In a one-horse o - pen sleigh!

You can accompany this jolly song with drums and bells.   After deciding what each instrument will play, you can write out a part for each performer.   Maybe you would like to write
a conductor's score like the scores for Small Drum and Big Drum on pages 3, 10, and 27.

Okum Daagya
(Stop-crying Song)

JANE ROLFE RANDOLPH

AMERICAN INDIAN
KIOWA TRIBE

A ha - wa ha___ wu wu A-go-go

Hunt-er bring-eth pa-poose good meat,
In dark wig-wam my watch I'll keep,

D.C. al Fine

Hush, lit-tle loud one, hush and eat.
Hush, lit-tle still one, go to sleep.

The Holy Man has performed the ceremony to gather in the game, and the mother has gone to kill an antelope. She has left her baby in the care of an old woman, who soothes the crying child with this song.

Aotzi No-otz
(Song of Victory)

AMERICAN INDIAN
CHEYENNE TRIBE

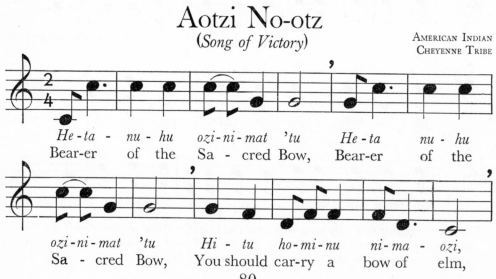

He-ta - nu-hu ozi-ni-mat 'tu He-ta nu-hu
Bear-er of the Sa-cred Bow, Bear-er of the

ozi-ni-mat 'tu Hi-tu ho-mi-nu ni-ma-ozi,
Sa-cred Bow, You should car-ry a bow of elm,

80

Hi - tu ho-mi-nu ni-ma- ozi, Hi yi ya!
You should car-ry a bow of elm! Hi yi ya!

The Sacred Bow was so holy that it never was allowed to touch the ground. No one was al-lowed to touch the Bow except the man appointed as its bearer. It was made of boxwood. It was in reproach that the song "Bearer of the Sacred Bow, You should carry a bow of elm!" was sung by a maiden whose lover had proved a coward.

Ceremonial Dance

JANE ROLFE RANDOLPH · AMERICAN INDIAN

Ge le la yah, ge le la yah, He__ hay you yah,
Big Chief read - y, Ea - gle Feath-er, Big_braves com-ing,
Through the for - est hear them com - ing, See_ them leap-ing,

a ka wan da le__yah, Yea ho! Yea ho! Ha_ na you sah
com-ing all to-geth - er, Yah ho! Yah ho! Big_Chief wait-ing
lis-ten to the drum-ming, Yah ho! Yah ho! Big_Chief wait-ing,

ha la nay__ you Oo ji - te yea noo he you Yoh!____
by the fire,____ Calls as the flames leap high - er, Yoh!____
Ea - gle Feath-er, Calls all the braves to-geth - er, Yoh!____

Voice study. Sing these tones in higher and lower keys.

Yoh!____ Yoh!____

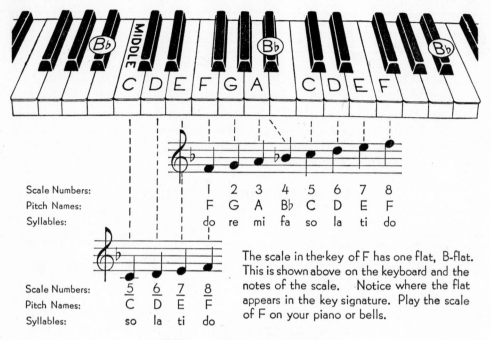

Scale Numbers:	1 2 3 4 5 6 7 8
Pitch Names:	F G A B♭ C D E F
Syllables:	do re mi fa so la ti do

Scale Numbers:	5̲ 6̲ 7̲ 8̲
Pitch Names:	C D E F
Syllables:	so la ti do

The scale in the key of F has one flat, B-flat. This is shown above on the keyboard and the notes of the scale. Notice where the flat appears in the key signature. Play the scale of F on your piano or bells.

The Bugle Call

From THE MODERN MUSIC SERIES

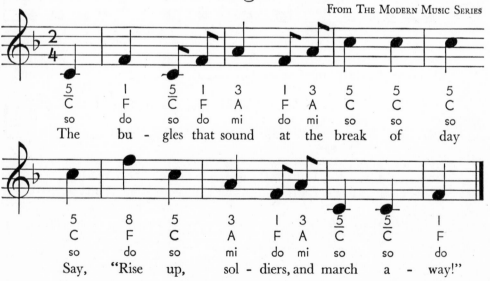

5̲	1	5̲	1	3	1	3	5	5	5
C	F	C	F	A	F	A	C	C	C
so	do	so	do	mi	do	mi	so	so	so

The bu- gles that sound at the break of day

5	8	5	3	1	3	5̲	5̲	1
C	F	C	A	F	A	C	C	F
so	do	so	mi	do	mi	so	so	do

Say, "Rise up, sol - diers, and march a - way!"

A Modern Dragon

Rowena Bastin Bennett

J. R. Weber

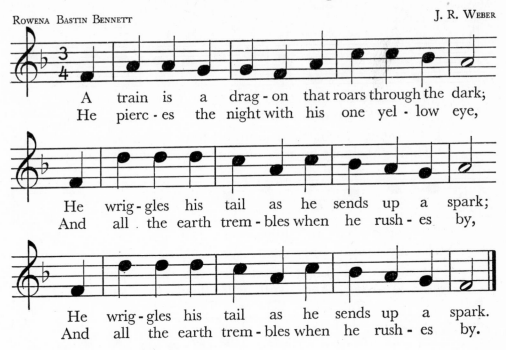

A train is a drag-on that roars through the dark;
He pierc-es the night with his one yel-low eye,

He wrig-gles his tail as he sends up a spark;
And all the earth trem-bles when he rush-es by,

He wrig-gles his tail as he sends up a spark.
And all the earth trem-bles when he rush-es by.

The Golden Rule
(Round)

Emerson and Tilden

Be to oth-ers ev-er kind and ev-er true,

As you'd have them ev-er faith-ful be to you.

O Morning Star!

Paraphrased from the original GERMAN by
NANCY BYRD TURNER

JOHANN SEBASTIAN BACH

O Morn-ing Star, thou Love of God, Thy beau-ty bright-ens
The world was dark in oth - er days, But now, O Morn-ing

O Star, a - bove an hum-ble town A-cross the world, thy
That light shines on up - on our way, It guides our trust-ing

all our road, It shines on hill and hol - low.)
Star, thy rays Are clear for us to fol - low.)

light came down, Long years a - go, and pure - ly)
feet to - day, And still will lead us sure - ly.)

Ho - ly! Ho - ly! Night has end-ed, fair and splen-did
Ho - ly! Ho - ly! Star of morn-ing, sky a-dorn-ing,

Light is show - ing, We are safe in all our go - ing.
Fail-ing nev - er, Love of God, to lead us ev - er.

The Night Sky
(Two-part Round)

ELLA D. WATKINS

The heav-ens are so ver- y_fair With star-ry can-dles gleam-ing there.

Prayer Before Battle

Harriet Auber
Paraphrased by Virginia Harrison

A. Williams

1. Sweet is the task, O__ Lord, Thy__ glo - rious__acts to sing,
2. We glad - ly stand and__raise The__songs that__tell Thy worth,
3. And gen - tly on our__hearts We__ feel Thy__bless-ing fall,

To praise Thy name, and hear Thy word, And grate-ful__ of-f'rings bring.
Then bow and ask Thy bless-ing, Lord, On us and__all the earth.
And know Thine ev - er - last- ing love Is round a - bout us all.

Sometimes two eighth notes are sung to one word or to one syllable of a word. There are two ways to show this: (1) by using a slur; (2) by using a crossbeam. Find the places in PRAYER BEFORE BATTLE where two eighth notes are sung to one word or to one syllable of a word. How are these eighth notes printed?

We Shall Follow One Another

Translated from the Russian
by Stella Marek Cushing

Singing Game from Russia

We shall_fol - low one an - oth - er Round and round a cir-cle gay,
No one_drag-ging, no one_lag- ging, Ev-'ry - one is now in line,

Ev- 'ry - thing that_Val-ya_shows us We re- peat it___ all to-day.
All is_good that_Val-ya_teach-es, We shall make a___ neat de-sign.

Can you make up a game of your own, following the words of the song?

The Song of the Lark

Alice Whitson Norton

Arr. from Ludwig van Beethoven

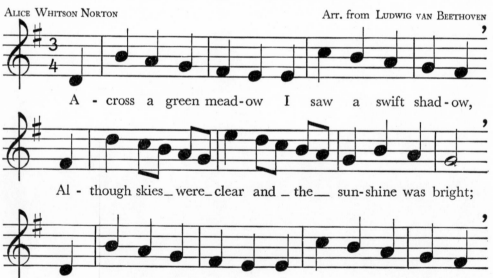

A - cross a green mead-ow I saw a swift shad-ow,

Al - though skies_were_clear and _ the_ sun-shine was bright;

But when I heard trill-ing a bird song so thrill-ing

I knew there was pass-ing a lark in his flight.

Ring Game

Nancy Byrd Turner

Folk Tune from Sweden

The girl takes__a__ rib-bon and ties it a-round
He takes the__red__ rib-bon and binds her, and then

The eyes of__ her__ part-ner, and, when he is bound,
We cir-cle,__ all__ sing-ing, and cir-cle a-gain,

As hand in hand we cir-cle and sing,
Now she must find a boy to be bound

An-oth-er girl he pulls in the ring.
While still we sing and cir-cle a-round.

The words of the song tell you how it should be danced.

Mr. Squirrel's Wedding

From the GREEK
by ANDRONIKE MEKELATOS

SINGING GAME from GREECE

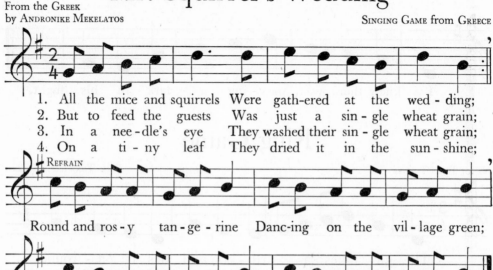

1. All the mice and squirrels Were gath-ered at the wed - ding;
2. But to feed the guests Was just a sin - gle wheat grain;
3. In a nee-dle's eye They washed their sin - gle wheat grain;
4. On a ti - ny leaf They dried it in the sun - shine;

REFRAIN

Round and ros-y tan-ge-rine Danc-ing on the vil-lage green;

Round and ros-y tan-ge-rine Will you be my vil-lage queen?

5. In a spindle hole
They ground the little wheat grain.

6. Then to pack the flour
They used a sack of bug-skin.

7. Then the sack of flour
Was loaded on a flea's back.

8. Ladies made the bread
While all the men admired them.

The Sparrow on the Eaves

From the FINNISH by
MARTHA DABNEY

FOLK SONG from FINLAND

Once I____ heard, when __ rain was fall - ing,
So I____ got up__ bright and ear - ly,

Heard a spar - row___ cheep - ing sad - ly,
Scat - tered grain and__ fed him glad - ly;

"I'm so hun-gry," he was call-ing
"Thank you, thank you for the bar-ley!"

From the eaves the whole day long.
Now he sings a hap-py song.

Big Bunch, a Little Bunch

Folk Game-Song
arranged by John W. Work

Big bunch, a lit-tle bunch, big bunch o' ros-es,

Big bunch, a lit-tle bunch, big bunch o' ros-es.

Here stands my wag-on team, Here stands my lard-stand,

Here stands my Val-en-tine, Here stands my dar-ling.

The children form a circle with one child in the center. They march around with hands joined as they sing. They stop at the word "roses." The child in the center points to three children as he sings. One is his "wagon team," another, his "lard-stand," and another, his "Valentine." When he comes to "my darling," he pulls the child into the center of the circle. He takes her place in the circle and the game starts again.

PLAYING THE CLARINET

The clarinet is a long pipe with a mouthpiece at one end. Fastened to this mouthpiece is a small, thin, flat reed, sliced from a bamboo stalk. When blown just right, this reed vibrates and causes the tone you hear. All up and down the clarinet are keys and levers. These are fingered to make the different tones, from the lowest to the highest.

Most clarinets are made in the key of B-flat. The written notes for the B-flat clarinet sound one whole step lower than the same notes would sound on the piano. Because of this, a separate part must be written for the clarinet. Some of you will wish to join your friends in the orchestra or band as players of the clarinet.

WRITTEN RANGE
OF THE CLARINET

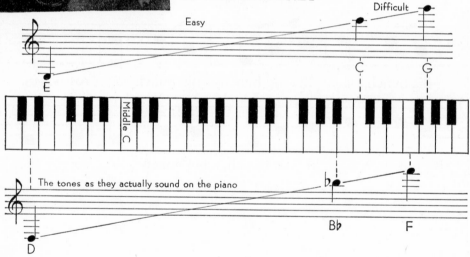

Someone who plays the clarinet can play this theme for you.

THEME
From "Menuet," E-flat Symphony

WOLFGANG AMADEUS MOZART

When played by the B-flat clarinet, this melody sounds in the key of E-flat, a whole step lower than the written notes.

90

Going to School

E. RICHTER

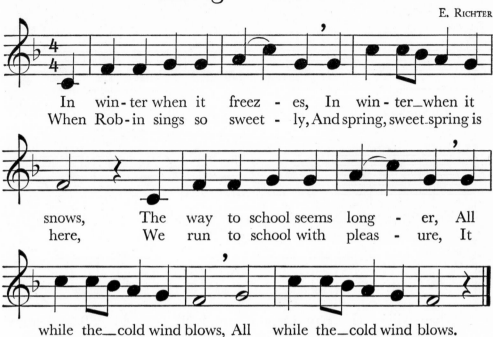

In win-ter when it freez - es, In win-ter_when it
When Rob-in sings so sweet - ly, And spring, sweet_spring is

snows, The way to school seems long - er, All
here, We run to school with pleas - ure, It

while the_cold wind blows, All while the_cold wind blows.
seems so__ver - y near, It seems so__ver - y near.

Going to School

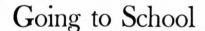

Going to School

Part for
Clarinet in B♭

E. RICHTER

What do you notice about the key of the song and the key of the clarinet part?
The clarinet part has been transposed to a key one whole step higher.
Clarinet players should learn to transpose their music so that they can play with singers or with
  the piano.

Oranges and Lemons

TRADITIONAL   ENGLISH

Orang-es and lem-ons, say the bells of St. Clem-en's;

You owe me five far-things, say the bells of St. Mar-tin's;

When will you pay me? say the bells of Old Bai-ley;

When I grow rich, say the bells of Shore-ditch;

When will that be? say the bells of Step-ney;

I do not know, says the great bell of Bow.

Here comes a can - dle to__ light you to bed,

And here comes a chop-per to__ chop off your head!

Gaily the Troubadour

T. H. BAYLY

T. H. BAYLY

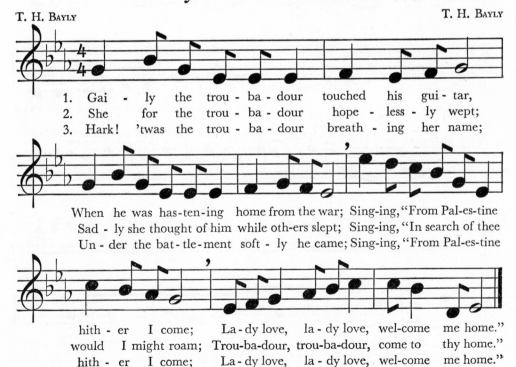

1. Gai - ly the trou - ba - dour touched his gui - tar,
2. She for the trou - ba - dour hope - less - ly wept;
3. Hark! 'twas the trou - ba - dour breath - ing her name;

When he was has-ten-ing home from the war; Sing-ing, "From Pal-es-tine
Sad - ly she thought of him while oth-ers slept; Sing-ing, "In search of thee
Un - der the bat-tle-ment soft-ly he came; Sing-ing, "From Pal-es-tine

hith - er I come; La - dy love, la - dy love, wel-come me home."
would I might roam; Trou-ba-dour, trou-ba-dour, come to thy home."
hith - er I come; La - dy love, la - dy love, wel-come me home."

CEREMONIAL AND BALLROOM DANCES

Allegro furioso, ma non troppo   Theme: WAR DANCE, from "TWO INDIAN DANCES" — SKILTON

Theme: INTERMEZZO, from "FAIRY TALES" — SUK

MENUET, from SYMPHONY IN E-FLAT — MOZART. See Theme on page 90.

Whistle When It Rains

William H. Blake   William H. Blake

1. The clouds are dark and it's rain-ing out-side,
2. The rain is good for the flow-ers and food,
3. Some-where the sun is___ shin-ing to - day,

So let's whis-tle a tune
So let's whis-tle a tune;
So let's whis-tle a tune,

To show the sun is___ shin-ing in - side.
Then you should be in a ver-y mer-ry mood.
And tap your feet to___ show___you're gay.

(Whistle or hum)_____

WHISTLE WHEN IT RAINS shows how music is printed when the verses have a different
number of words. Find the words, "and it's," in the first line of the song. There are two
eighth notes for these two words. At this same place, the third verse has only one word,
"is." The slur joins these two eighth notes for the third verse.

Sometimes the curved line is called a *tie*. This is when it joins two notes on the same line
or space of the staff.

Find two places in this song where a slur is used and two places where a tie is used.

95

96 I Have Lost the "do" on My Clarinet

(*J'ai perdu le do de ma Clarinette*)

FRENCH FOLK SONG

I have lost the "do" on my clar - i - net,_____
J'ai per - du le do de ma cla - ri - net - te,

I have lost the "do" on my clar - i - net,_____
J'ai per - du le do de ma cla - ri - net - te,

Ah, if Pa - pa on - ly knew! Tra la la!
Ah, si Pa - pa sa - vait ça, tra la la!

Ah, if Pa - pa on - ly knew! Tra la la! March
Ah, si Pa - pa sa - vait ça, tra la la! , Au

on, tra la la, march on, tra la la, Keep step and sing our song; March
pas, ca - ma - rade, au pas, ca - ma - rade, Au pas, au pas, au pas! Au

on, tra la la, march on, tra la la, Keep step and march a - long!
pas, ca - ma - rade, au pas, ca - ma - rade, Au pas, au pas, au pas!

When you sing the song a second time, you lose "re." Each time you repeat, you lose the
next note of the scale.

Fun at the Zoo

NANCY BYRD TURNER

CZECH FOLK SONG

Come with me, and you'll see crea-tures cheer-y mak-ing mer-ry,
There's an ox with a fox, and a don-key with a mon-key,

Fat rac-coon, laugh-ing loon, waltz-ing with a big ba-boon,
While a whale and a quail step po-lite - ly 'round a snail,

And a romp-y tom-boy ta-pir cut-ting ev-'ry kind of ca-per,
And a wad-dly, tod-dly hip-po hol-lers, "Part-ner, come and skip-o!"

And a bear with a hare whirl-ing mad-ly, glad-ly there.
You'll a-gree soon with me, this was quite a jam-bo-ree!

Polka Step: Step forward with right foot; close left foot to right foot; step forward with right foot; hop with right foot (first measure). Same movements, beginning with left foot (second measure). Continue, changing feet with each measure.

You can polka step to this song while clapping the note patterns.

Rhythm of the Polka

Continue with your own pattern to fit the rest of the song.

Roadways

John Masefield

Francis de Bourguignon

1. One road leads to Lon - don, One road leads to Wales,

My road leads me sea - ward To the white dip-ping sails,

To the white dip - ping sails.

From POEMS by John Masefield. By permission of The Macmillan Company, Publishers.

2. One road leads to the river,
   As it goes swinging slow,
   My road leads to shipping,
   Where bronzed sailors go.

3. Lures me, lures me, calls me
   To salt green tossing sea;
   A road without earth's road dust
   Is the right road for me.

4. A wet road, heaving, shining,
   And wild with the sea gull's cries;
   A mad salt sea-wind blowing
   The salt spray in my eyes.

Village Dance

VIRGINIA HARRISON

Tambourine part

CZECH FOLK SONG

O-pen wide the win-dow and you'll hear
Ev-'ry-bod-y knows the tune they play,

Sound of jol-ly mu-sic draw-ing near;
All will find their part-ners right a - way;

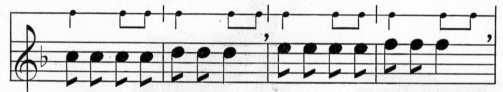

Fid-dle loud and tam-bou-rine Play-ing on the vil-lage green.
Tam-bou-rines will beat the time, "Tump-ty, tump-ty," like a rhyme,

O-pen wide the win-dow and you'll hear
Ev-'ry-bod-y knows the tune they play,

Sound of jol-ly mu-sic draw-ing near!
All will find their part-ners right a - way.

The Measure Rest (▬) occurs four times in this song. The time signature tells us that for
each measure rest the voices do not sing for two beats.

Rider

Nancy Byrd Turner

Kay Kellogg

Young Wash-ing-ton had nev-er heard Of a
Young Wash-ing-ton had roads to ride That were

mo-tor car or a train; He would-n't have un-der-
full of ruts and of rocks, With ditch-es and banks on

stood a word A-bout an___ aer-o-plane; But
ei-ther side And___ mud to his hor-se's hocks; But

gal-lo-py, gal-o-py, how he went gal-lop-ing
gal-lo-py, gal-o-py, how he went gal-lop-ing,

Up hill, down dale, wind in his hair; Straight-ly a-strad-dle with
Bay colt, gray colt, sor-rel or roan; Bri-dle rein flash-ing and

nev-er a sad-dle, Gal-lop-ing ev-'ry-where!
red___ mud splash-ing, Gal-lop-ing on and on!

Farmyard Song

TRADITIONAL

KENTUCKY MOUNTAIN FOLK SONG

1. I had a cat, and the cat pleased me,
2. I had a hen, and the hen pleased me,
3. I had a duck, and the duck pleased me,

I fed my cat by yon-der tree;
I fed my hen by yon-der tree;
I fed my duck by yon-der tree;

First ending   Fine.

Cat goes fid-dle-i - fee!

Second ending

Hen goes chim-my-chuck, chim-my-chuck!

Here repeat first ending and then go back to third verse.

Third ending

Duck goes quack,   quack!

Here repeat second ending, then first ending and then
go on to fourth verse. The endings for the following verses are repeated in the same way.

4. I had a goose

Goose goes his - sy, his - sy!

5. I had a sheep

Sheep goes baa, baa!

6. I had a hog

Hog goes squeel-y, squeel-y!

7. I had a cow

Cow goes moo, moo!

8. I had a horse

Horse goes neigh, neigh!

9. I had a dog

Dog goes bow-wow, bow-wow!

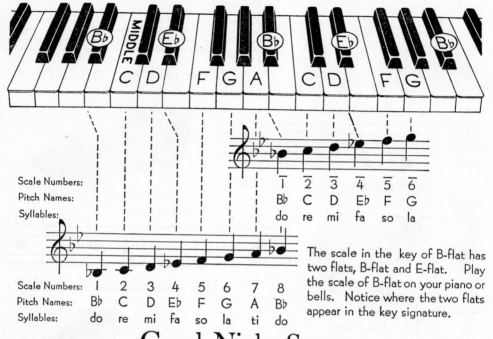

The scale in the key of B-flat has two flats, B-flat and E-flat. Play the scale of B-flat on your piano or bells. Notice where the two flats appear in the key signature.

Good Night Song

From the original LETT by
AILEEN FISHER

FOLK SONG from LATVIA

5	5	5	5	6	6	6	6	7	7	7	7	8	8	8
F	F	F	F	G	G	G	G	A	A	A	A	Bb	Bb	Bb
so	so	so	so	la	la	la	la	ti	ti	ti	ti	do	do	do

Dark-ness fills the tops of fir trees When the sun has sunk from sight,

2	4	3	3	3	2	2	2	2	1	1	1
C	Eb	D	D	D	C	C	C	C	Bb	Bb	Bb
re	fa	mi	mi	mi	re	re	re	re	do	do	do

Ai,　ai,　through the night,　When the sun has　sunk from sight.

Song of the Clock

NADINE BENSLEY KEYES   NADINE BENSLEY KEYES

"Tick - tock, tick - tock," sings the clock,

Al - ways tick - ing, not a stop,

All day long and all night, too,

Ev - 'ry day the long hours through.

"Tick - tock, tick - tock," sings the clock,

Al - ways tick - ing, not a stop.

Voice study. The last two lines of this song make a fine study for
voices. Sing them with "tick-tock," "ho, ho," and with the words
of the song. Sing in higher and lower keys.

The Birds' Ball

NURSERY RHYME   TRADITIONAL

1. Spring once said   to the night-in-gale, "I mean to   give you
2. Soon they came   from bush and tree,   Sing-ing sweet their

birds   a   ball,   Pray, ma'am, ask the birdies   all,   The
songs of   glee;   Each one fresh from his co-zy   nest.

old   and young, the great and small."   Tra   la   la la la,
Each one dressed in his Sun-day best.   Tra   la   la la la,

Tra   la   la la la,   Tra   la   la la la,   Tra la la la la,

Tra la la la la, Tra la la la la,

Tra la la la la la la la la la.

3. The wren and the cuckoo danced for life,
   The raven waltzed with the yellow-bird's wife,
   The awkward owl and the bashful jay
   Wished each other a very good day.
   Tra la la la la etc.

4. The woodpecker came from his hole in the tree,
   And brought his bill to the company
   For cherries ripe and berries red;
   'Twas a very long bill, so the birds all said
   Tra la la la la etc.

5. They danced all day till the sun was low,
   And mother birds prepared to go;
   Then one and all, both great and small,
   Flew home to their nests from the birdies' ball.
   Tra la la la la etc.

Rhythm of the Schottische

Gaily, but not too quickly

Beats

Small Drum

Big Drum

Schottische Step: Step, step, step, hop, as you count 1, 2, 3, 4.

Roses from the South

ALICE WHITSON NORTON

JOHANN STRAUSS

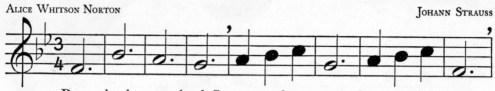

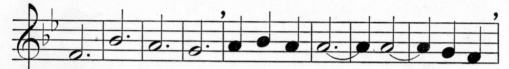

Rose - bud, rose - bud, Sweet south-ern rose, beau-ti -ful   rose;

Do you sleep, sweet, Through win-ter snows,—— South - ern rose?

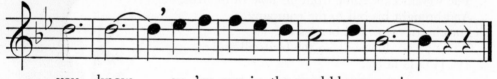

And when wak - ing, Tell me, please do, And tell me true, Do

you know____ ev - 'ry-one in the world loves you!____

Waltz Step with partners (see page 38): Boy and girl face, both hands joined.   Girl starts
right foot, boy starts left foot. Girl goes backward, boy goes forward two phrases. Repeat,
in opposite direction.

You can waltz to this song while clapping the note patterns.

A pleasing effect will be produced by a light Triangle tap on the first beat of each measure.

Triangle part for "Roses from the South"

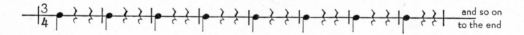

and so on
to the end

We're Going Round the Mountain

AMERICAN SINGING GAME

1. We're go-ing round the moun-tain, two by two,

We're go-ing round the moun-tain, two by two,

We're go-ing round the moun-tain, two by two,

Continue without pause

This measure has only one beat.

So rise, Sal-ly, rise.

2. Let me see you make a motion, two by two.
3. That's a pretty poor motion, two by two.
4. Let me see you make another one, two by two.
5. That's a very good motion, two by two.

Circle game with odd player. Players form a circle; odd player squats in center.

Verse 1: Players march in a circle, singing and clapping.

Verses 2, 3, 4: Odd player follows words of stanzas, making any sort of motion he wishes.

Verse 5: Players resume their march. Odd player chooses someone from the circle with whom he changes places. The game begins again.

Elephants

LENORE M. LINK

CLARE E. GRUNDMAN

1. El - e-phants walk-ing a - long___the trails
2. Trunks_and tails___ are hand - y things
3. El - e-phants work___ and el - e-phants play,

Are hold - ing hands by hold - ing tails.
When el-e-phants walk in cir - cus rings.
And el-e-phants walk and feel so gay.

And when they walk It nev - er fails,

They're hold - ing hands by hold - ing tails.

A Little Bit of Anything

TRADITIONAL

MARSHALL BARTHOLOMEW

Here's a streak o' lean And there's a streak o' fat,

There's a good old 'pos - sum, I'll take a piece o' that.

Here's a plate o' bis - cuits, There's a plate o' pie,

Here's some good old corn bread That suits my eye.

There's a cup o' cof - fee, Here's a cup o' tea,

But there's a glass o' fresh milk That's good e-nough for me.

Snow-White

MARY MANNING

R. GRANER

1. Of Snow-White this is the sto - ry, Who strayed in for - est hoar - y;
2. As dark the night was near-ing, She came up - on a clear-ing
3. And soon this prin-cess maid-en, With hum-ble chores was lad - en;
4. She cooked them dain - ty dish - es, And baked to each dwarf's wish-es,
5. A prince, who heard the ru - mor, Set out in high good hu - mor;

Her hair was bright as yel - low gold, Her face was pale with
With sev - en dwarfs a-round a fire, Who ea - ger - ly did
She scrubbed till ev - 'ry-thing gleamed bright, The sev - en dwarfs beamed
She fed them tarts and cakes, a score, Un - til the dwarfs could
He found the prin-cess fair and meek, And they were wed with-

frost and cold, All wet with tears, Once up - on a time.____
ask her hire To serve them all, Once up - on a time.____
with de-light And danced with glee, Once up - on a time.____
eat no more Then fell a - sleep, Once up - on a time.____
in a week; So ran the tale, Once up - on a time.____

112

Shadow Pictures

Anna M. Priestley

Edward Bailey Birge

Shad-ow pic-tures on the wall, Some are short and some are tall;

Some are thin and some are fat, Bark-ing dog and yawn - ing cat,

Long-eared rab-bit, long-nosed man, Make them life-like as you can;

Make them jump and make them run, Shad-ow pic-tures are such fun!

Chinese Farmer's Song
(Ch'u T'ou Ko)

Arranged by C. H. Y. CHEN

Now with our hoe we till the fields, hei!
Shou pa cho ch'u t'ou ch'u yeh ts'ao ya!

Rid all our fields of — wick-ed weeds, — hei!
Ch'u ch'u liao yeh ts'ao — hao chang miao_____ ya!

Yi - ya - hei, Ya - hu - hei!

Now we will rid our fields of the weeds, — Ya-
Ch'u ch'u liao yeh_____ ts'ao hao chang miao,_____ ya!

hu - hei, *Ya - hu - hei!*

Hey, Little Boy!

Collected by MARY NEWCOMB

KENTUCKY FOLK SONG
Collected by NOEL MARCHANT

1,2,3,4,

Hey, lit - tle boy! Yes, Ma'am.
Been to the pic-nic? Yes, Ma'am.
See my girl? Yes, Ma'am.
Court my girl? Yes, Ma'am.
When you goin' to mar-ry?

5.

Soon next Tues - day morn-ing, oh,

Soon next Tues - day morn-ing, oh,

Soon next Tues - day morn-ing, oh,

Soon next Tues - day morn-ing, oh.

Hey, little boy! Yes, Ma'am.
Been to the barn? Yes, Ma'am.
See my mare? Yes, Ma'am.
Feed my mare? Yes, Ma'am.
Curry my mare? Yes, Ma'am.
Ride my mare? Yes, Ma'am.

How'd she ride?
She rocked just like a cradle, oh,
She rocked just like a cradle, oh,
She rocked just like a cradle, oh,
She rocked just like a cradle, oh.

You can add some verses of your own.

115

Tell Me, Shepherdess

NANCY BYRD TURNER

FRENCH CANADIAN FOLK SONG

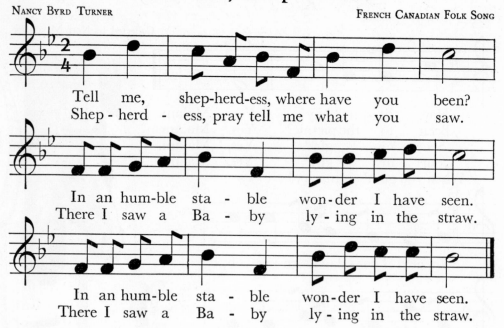

Tell me, shep-herd-ess, where have you been?
Shep - herd - ess, pray tell me what you saw.

In an hum-ble sta - ble won-der I have seen.
There I saw a Ba - by ly - ing in the straw.

In an hum-ble sta - ble won-der I have seen.
There I saw a Ba - by ly - ing in the straw.

Study TELL ME, SHEPHERDESS, and notice which phrases are alike and which are different. Then write the letters to show the phrase pattern. You will see that each stanza really consists of two lines of poetry, the second line being repeated. That is why the music of the second and third phrases must be similar.

Here are some poems of two lines each to which you can make up an A, B, B' tune. Then your teacher can help you write it.

Every rose on the little tree
Is making a different face at me.

Rachel Field

Rainbow at night is the sailor's delight;
Rainbow at morning, sailors, take warning.

Old Rhyme

A rosy cloud of the dawn I see
Entangled there in the almond tree.

Charles Dalmon

Now try making up your own poem and tune with the same phrase pattern as TELL ME, SHEPHERDESS.

Little Girl, Where Are You Going?

Paraphrased from the SPANISH by
JANE ROLFE RANDOLPH

SPANISH AMERICAN FOLK TUNE

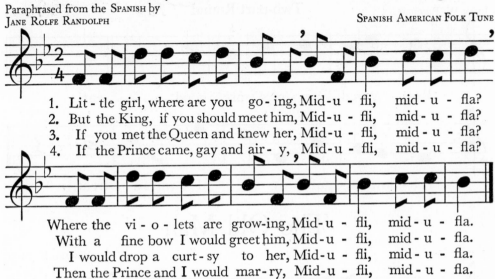

1. Lit - tle girl, where are you go - ing, Mid-u - fli, mid - u - fla?
2. But the King, if you should meet him, Mid-u - fli, mid - u - fla?
3. If you met the Queen and knew her, Mid-u - fli, mid - u - fla?
4. If the Prince came, gay and air - y, Mid-u - fli, mid - u - fla?

Where the vi - o - lets are grow-ing, Mid-u - fli, mid - u - fla.
With a fine bow I would greet him, Mid-u - fli, mid - u - fla.
I would drop a curt - sy to her, Mid-u - fli, mid - u - fla.
Then the Prince and I would mar - ry, Mid-u - fli, mid - u - fla.

Study the four phrases of LITTLE GIRL, WHERE ARE YOU GOING? Find the phrases which are alike and those which are different.   Then write the letters to show the phrase pattern.   See if you can find other songs in this book with the same phrase pattern.   Here is a poem with a phrase pattern like LITTLE GIRL, WHERE ARE YOU GOING? You can make up your own tune for this poem.   Then your teacher can help you write it.

> God, in all your heavenly goodness,
> Guard my mother dear.
> Shower down on her your blessings,
> Keep her happy here.
>
> *Edna Hansen* (Fifth Grade)

Here is a poem for which it would be better to use a different phrase pattern. Can you decide what the phrase pattern should be, and then write the tune?

> The time of day I like the best
> Is when the sun sets in the west,
> And all the sky is painted red,
> And Mister Sun prepares for bed.
>
> *Patsy Leonard* (Fourth Grade)

Now try making up your own poem as well as your own tune.   You will find songs in this book with many different phrase patterns.   In your own songs you can use whatever phrase patterns you wish.   It is usually best, however, to repeat at least one of the phrases.   The repeated phrases can be exactly alike, or nearly alike.

Fruit

Two-part Round

JULIA W. BINGHAM

L. W. MASON

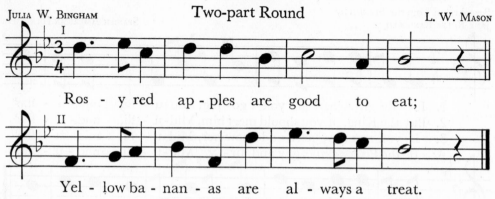

Ros - y red ap - ples are good to eat;

Yel - low ba - nan - as are al - ways a treat.

The Old Man

EDWARD LEAR

EDWARD B. BIRGE

There was an old man with a beard,_Who said, "It is just as I feared!_

Two owls and a hen, Four larks and a wren,

Have all built their nests in my beard!"_

There was an old man in a tree
Who was horribly bored by a bee;
When they said, "Does it buzz?"
He replied, "Yes, it does!
It's a regular bore of a bee."

DAY MUSIC AND NIGHT MUSIC

Theme: GONDOLIERS, from "A DAY IN VENICE" — NEVIN

Reprinted by permission of the John Church Company, publishers and copyright owners.

Theme: SCHERZO, from "A MIDSUMMER NIGHT'S DREAM" — MENDELSSOHN

John the Rabbit

FOLK GAME-SONG
arranged by JOHN W. WORK

Old John the rab-bit, O, yes! Old John the rab-bit, O, yes!

Got a might-y bad hab-it, O, yes! Of go-ing to my gar-den,

O, yes! And eat-ing up my peas, O, yes! And cut-ting down my cab-bage,

O, yes! He ate to-ma-toes, O, yes! And sweet po-ta-toes,

O, yes! And if I live, O, yes! To see next fall,

O, yes! I won't plant, O, yes! A gar-den at all!

A leader sings and is answered by the group, "O, yes!"
The group clap hands throughout the song. They may stand in a circle, with the leader in the
center. At the end of the song the group may choose a new leader and begin again.

Boat Song

Nancy Byrd Turner

Folk Song

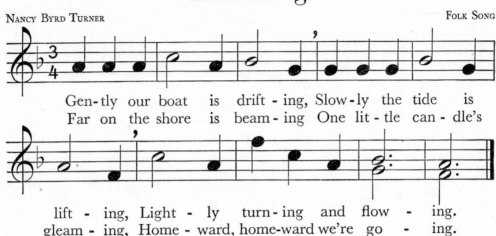

Gen-tly our boat is drift-ing, Slow-ly the tide is
Far on the shore is beam-ing One lit-tle can-dle's

lift - ing, Light - ly turn-ing and flow - ing.
gleam - ing, Home - ward, home-ward we're go - ing.

Tideo

Traditional

Singing Game from Texas

Skip one win-dow, Ti - de - o, Skip two win-dows, Ti - de - o,

Skip three win-dows, Ti - de - o, Jin-gle at the win-dows, Ti - de - o.

Jin-gling, jin-gling, jin-gling Joe, Jin-gle at the win-dows, Ti - de - o.

TIDEO is a double-circle game. Players choose partners. Girls stand in a circle, facing out-ward. Boys form a larger circle, facing the girls.

When the song begins, the boys face right and start marching around the circle of girls. When each boy reaches his partner, he swings her by the right hand. The boys then march around again. This time the boy swings the girl that he meets just before his partner. When each boy has swung all the girls, boys and girls change places. The game may begin again.

How the Corn Grows

Dorris Cosford

Czech Folk Tune

1. When corn be - gins___ to sprout,___ Two lit - tle
2. The stalks will tall - er grow___ And ti - ny
3. And when the silk___ is spun___ It's col - ored

leaves___ peep out;___ Then when the leaves___ are
ears___ will show;___ Then when the ears___ are
by___ the sun;___ Then when the au - tumn

fresh and green A slen - der stalk shoots up be -
long and thin The pret - ty silk be - gins to
air is chill The corn is read - y for the

tween,___Then when the leaves___ are fresh and green
spin, ___Then when the ears ___ are long and thin
mill,___Then when the au - tumn air is chill

A stalk shoots up be - tween.___
The silk be - gins to spin.___
It's read - y for the mill.___

An Old Fairy Tale

Paraphrased from the FRENCH by
JANE ROLFE RANDOLPH

FOLK SONG from SAVOY

1. 'Neath an ap - ple tree sat May, Rock - ing, rock - ing all day;
2. Came a hand-some prince that way, Sing - ing, sing - ing all day;

'Neath an ap - ple tree sat May, Rock - ing, rock - ing all day;
Came a hand-some prince that way, Sing - ing, sing - ing all day;

While a rob - in high___ a - bove
Saw the maid - en sit - ting there

Sang a song of gen - tle love,
All so neat and sweet___ and fair,

Rock - ing, rock - ing all day.
Sing - ing, sing - ing all day.

3. Not a word she found to say,
Laughing, laughing all day;
Not a word she found to say,
Laughing, laughing all day;
But he took her by the hand,
Led her to his castle grand,
Laughing, laughing all day.

4. They were wed the royal way,
Happy, happy all day;
They were wed the royal way,
Happy, happy all day;
She a queen and he a king,
Loud the wedding bells did ring,
Happy, happy all day.

PLAYING THE CORNET (TRUMPET)

The cornet belongs to a family of very old instruments. For thousands of years this type of instrument has called people to worship. With its bright, ringing tones it has called armies to the defense of their homeland.

The cornet and the trumpet are much alike. Both instruments are played the same way. Each is made of a long tube that is coiled so that it can be held in the hand comfortably. The tones are made by blowing into a mouthpiece. The boy above is playing the trumpet.

The cornet is usually made in the key of B-flat. Like the clarinet, it must have a special part written so that its tones will fit with those of the piano.

WRITTEN RANGE OF THE CORNET (TRUMPET)
(Some soloists can play even higher)

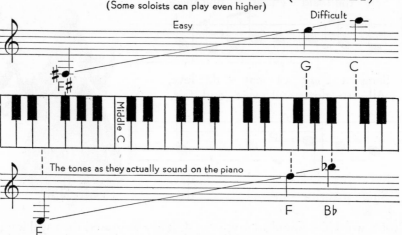

Someone who plays the cornet can play TAPS and REVEILLE for you.

Taps

This is the call that ends the soldier's day.

124

Reveille

United States Armed Forces Bugle Call

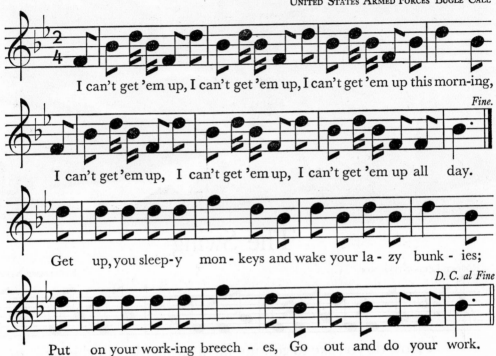

I can't get 'em up, I can't get 'em up, I can't get 'em up this morn-ing,

Fine.

I can't get 'em up, I can't get 'em up, I can't get 'em up all day.

Get up, you sleep-y mon - keys and wake your la - zy bunk - ies;

D. C. al Fine

Put on your work-ing breech - es, Go out and do your work.

Reveille

This is the call that wakes the soldiers in the morning.

Cornet in B♭

Fine.

D. C. al Fine

The Swing

Robert Louis Stevenson

Ethelbert Nevin

How do you like to go up in a swing, Up in the air so blue?____ Oh, I do think it's the pleas-ant-est thing Ev-er a child can do.____ Up in the air and o-ver the wall Till I can see so wide,__ Riv-ers and trees and cat-tle and all

126

O-ver the coun-try-side,

Till I look down on the gar-den green,

Down on the roof so brown, Up in the air I go fly-ing a-gain,

Up in the air and down, and down, Up in the air and down.

127

Beautiful Bells

MARY MANNING

HENRY ROWLEY BISHOP

Chime a-gain, chime a-gain, beau - ti - ful bells,

Lin - ger a while o'er the deep dusk - y bay;

Faint - er and faint - er thy mel - o - dy swells,

Fast fades the land, and thy sounds die a - way.

Beats
Note
Patterns

and so on
to the end

All through the Night

TRADITIONAL

OLD WELSH MELODY

Sleep, my child, and peace at-tend thee All through the night;

Guard - ian an - gels God will send thee All through the night;

Soft the drow-sy hours are creep-ing, Hill and vale in slum-ber steep-ing;

I my lov - ing vig - il keep - ing All through the night.

Beats

Note Patterns $\frac{4}{4}$ and so on to the end

My Mountain

Nancy Byrd Turner

Czech Folk Song

One high moun-tain that I know   Of-ten wears a coat of green;
Then a cap of mist, in-stead;   But I like my moun-tain best

Then a-gain in brown is seen, Some-times wears a cap of snow.
When in eve-ning blue 'tis dressed, With a star up-on its head.

Dotted Quarter and Eighth Notes

The Dotted Quarter Note is held while we make two beats, and then the Eighth Note is sung quickly. The next following note comes with the next following beat.

You can step to these songs while clapping the note patterns.

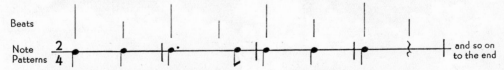

Beats

Note Patterns $\frac{2}{4}$ and so on to the end

Rainbow

MARION J. DALY

A. LOUIS SCARMOLIN

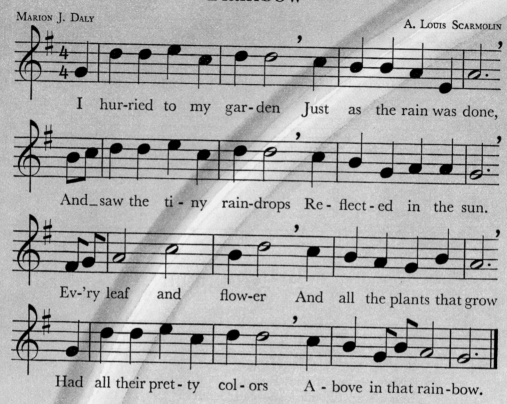

I hur-ried to my gar-den Just as the rain was done,

And saw the ti-ny rain-drops Re-flect-ed in the sun.

Ev-'ry leaf and flow-er And all the plants that grow

Had all their pret-ty col-ors A-bove in that rain-bow.

Brother Robin

MRS. ANDERSON

From THE NORMAL MUSIC COURSE

1. Lis-ten, in the A-pril rain, Broth-er Rob-in's here a-gain;

Songs, like show-ers, come and go, He is house-build-ing, I know.

CHORUS

Chip, chip, cheer-y, he is sing-ing, Light-ly on an elm twig swing-ing.

2. Though he finds the old pine tree
   Is not where it used to be,
   And the nest he made last year
   Torn and scattered far and near.
   (Chorus)

3. He has neither grief nor care;
   Building sites are everywhere;
   If one nest is blown away,
   Fields are full of sticks and hay.
   (Chorus)

4. Though old mousing puss, last year,
   Ate his little ones, I fear,
   And he almost died of fright,
   That is all forgotten quite.
   (Chorus)

Chorus: (Verse 2, 3, and 4)
Chip, chip, cheery,
He keeps singing,
Lightly on an elm twig swinging.

Voice study. Sing the chorus with tones as clear as a robin's. Sing in higher and lower keys. Sing other bird calls that you know, with very good tones, clear and ringing.

A Pledge

MARGARET MANN

WOLFGANG AMADEUS MOZART

I pledge my - self to love the right, The
good, the fair and true, To keep my faith and
hon - or bright In ev - 'ry - thing I do.

O Sanctissima

MEDIEVAL LATIN HYMN

OLD ITALIAN MELODY

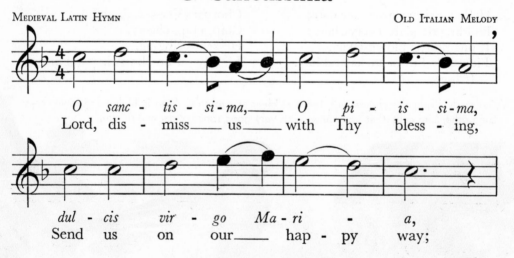

O sanc - tis - si - ma, O pi - is - si - ma,
Lord, dis - miss us with Thy bless - ing,

dul - cis vir - go Ma - ri - a,
Send us on our hap - py way;

ma - ter a - ma - ta, in - te - me - ra - ta,
Let__ Thy__ love, our hearts__ pos - sess - ing,

o - ra,____ o - ra pro no - bis.
Guide__ our____ steps__ from__ day to day.

Dancing the Mazurka

VIRGINIA HARRISON

OLD MAZURKA DANCE TUNE from POLAND

Fid-dles call, now, an-swer all, now, Dance the gay ma - zur - ka!
Keep the beat, boy, in your feet, boy, Dance the gay ma - zur - ka!

Tune's be-gun, now, join the fun, now, Slide to left and right, hey!
Get the swing, girl, and the fling, girl, Dance with all your might, hey!

Rhythm of the Mazurka

Vigorous. Slower than the Waltz but not as slow as the Minuet.
Notice the strong accent on the third beat of the measure. The tune ends on the second beat.

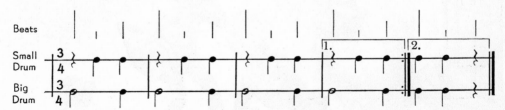

134 Dame, Get Up and Bake Your Pies

MOTHER GOOSE

TRADITIONAL

1. Dame, get up__ and bake your pies,

Bake your pies,   bake your pies;

Dame, get up__ and bake your pies,

So ear - ly in __ the morn - ing.

2. Dame, what makes your maidens lie?
3. Dame, what makes your ducks to die?
4. Their wings are cut, they cannot fly.

Oh, Fair to See

CHRISTINA G. ROSSETTI

MARSHALL BARTHOLOMEW

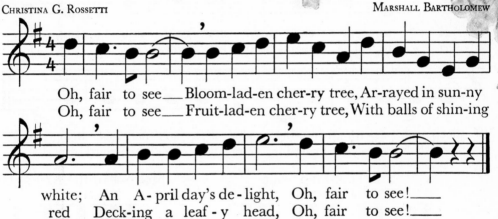

Oh, fair to see___ Bloom-lad-en cher-ry tree, Ar-rayed in sun-ny
Oh, fair to see___ Fruit-lad-en cher-ry tree, With balls of shin-ing

white; An A-pril day's de-light, Oh, fair to see!___
red Deck-ing a leaf-y head, Oh, fair to see!___

Amen

ARTHUR GUITERMAN

KAY KELLOGG

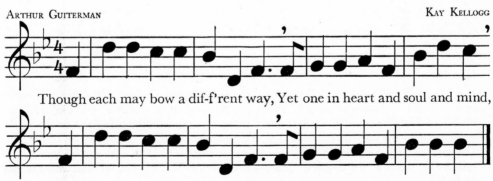

Though each may bow a dif-f'rent way, Yet one in heart and soul and mind,

Dear Fa-ther, hear Thy chil-dren pray For peace and love for all man-kind.

The Shepherdess
(*La Pastora*)

NANCY BYRD TURNER

SPANISH AMERICAN FOLK SONG

A shep-herd-ess goes sing - ing, La - rán, la - rán, la-
The shep-herd-ess comes sing - ing, La - rán, la - rán, la-

ri - to, A shep - herd - ess goes sing - ing, Her
ri - to, The shep - herd - ess comes sing - ing, Her

sheep to pas - ture bring-ing, Her sheep to pas - ture bring-ing.
flock she's home-ward bring-ing, Her flock she's home-ward bring-ing.

The Half-Step Scale

Sharp-4 in the Key of C

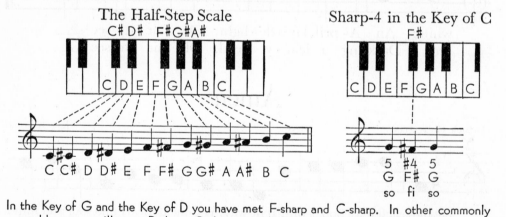

In the Key of G and the Key of D you have met F-sharp and C-sharp. In other commonly used keys you will meet D-sharp, G-sharp, and A-sharp. If you look at the diagram, "The Half-Step Scale", you will see where these tones are found on the piano and on the staff.

We can speak of the scale by numbers (1, 2, 3), by letters (c, d, e), or by syllables (*do, re, mi*). The sharp in THE SHEPHERDESS may be called sharp-four (#4), F-sharp (F #), or by the syllable *fi*. Look at the diagram, "Sharp-4 in the key of C", and you will see where it may be found.

You will see that sharps not only are found in different keys and their signatures, but that they are used also to add to the tonal variety and color of melodies.

The Blue Bells of Scotland

Annie McVicar

Old Scottish Air

1. Oh where, and oh where is your High-land lad-die gone?
2. Oh where, and oh where does your High-land lad-die dwell?
3. Oh what, tell me what does your High-land lad-die wear?

Oh where, and oh where is your High-land lad-die gone?
Oh where, and oh where does your High-land lad-die dwell?
Oh what, tell me what does your High-land lad-die wear?

He's gone to fight the foe, for King George up-on the throne;
He dwelt in mer-ry Scot-land, at the sign of the Blue Bell;
A bon-net with a feath-er, And on his breast a plaid.

And it's oh! in my heart how I wish him safe at home.
And it's oh! in my heart that I love my lad-die well.
And it's oh! in my heart that I love my High-land lad.

Sharp-4 in the Key of D

G#

F# C#

D E G A B D

5 #4 5
A G# A
so fi so

Voice study. This is a fine song to help you sing more beautiful tones. Sing the first phrase with "ho, ho," in higher
and lower keys. Then, as you sing them, float the words
on the tones.

CONTRASTING DANCES

Theme: MAZURKA, from the ballet "COPPELIA" — DELIBES

Tempo di Mazurka

Theme: GAVOTTE, "AMARYLLIS" — GHYS

Allegro moderato

DANCE OF THE HAPPY SPIRITS — GLUCK. See Theme on page 144.

Over the Hills and Far Away

OLD ENGLISH FOLK SONG

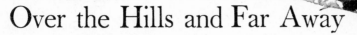

Tom_ he_ was_ a_ pip - er's son,

He learned to_ play_ when_ he was young;

But all_ the_ tune_that_ he could play

Was "O - ver the hills and_ far a - way."

O - ver the hills and a great way off,

The wind shall blow my_ top-knot off.

139

Hush! the Waves Are Rolling In

WHITTIER'S "CHILD LIFE"

OLD GAELIC LULLABY

Hush! the waves are roll - ing in, White with foam,

white with foam; Fa - ther toils a - mid the

din, But ba - by sleeps at home._____

Blow Away the Morning Dew

OLD ENGLISH FOLK SONG

1. Up - on the sweet-est sum-mer-time, In the mid-dle of the morn,
2. The yel-low cow-slip by the brim, The__ daf-fo-dil as well,
3. She's gone with all those flow-ers sweet, Of__white, of red, and blue,

A pret-ty dam-sel I es-pied, The fair-est ev-er born.
The tim-id prim-rose, pale and trim, The pret-ty snow-drop bell.
And un-to me a-bout my feet Is on-ly left the rue.

And sing, blow a-way the morn-ing dew, The dew, and the dew.

Blow a-way the morn-ing dew, How sweet the winds do blow.

Reprinted from *English Folk Songs for Schools,* Curwen Edition No. 6051, Collected and Edited by Cecil Sharp and S. Baring-Gould, by permission of J. Curwen & Sons, Ltd., London.

Twilight

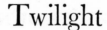

GRACE W. MORGAN

RUSSELL V. MORGAN

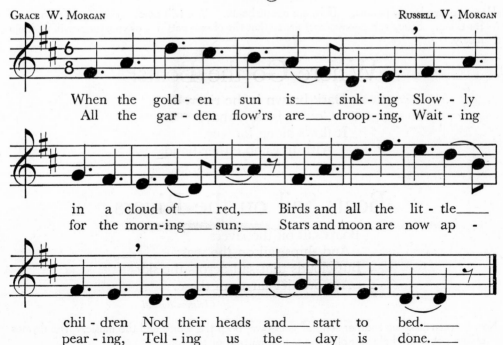

When the gold - en sun is____ sink - ing Slow - ly
All the gar - den flow'rs are____ droop - ing, Wait - ing

in a cloud of____ red,____ Birds and all the lit - tle____
for the morn - ing____ sun;____ Stars and moon are now ap -

chil - dren Nod their heads and____ start to bed.____
pear - ing, Tell - ing us the____ day is done.____

MAKING YOUR OWN TUNES

Here are two lovely poems. Both are about boats. You will enjoy making your own tunes for them. Study the poems carefully so that the phrase patterns of your tunes will fit them nicely.

Where Go the Boats?

Dark brown is the river,
Golden is the sand,
It flows along forever,
With trees on either hand.

Robert Louis Stevenson

Boats Sail on the Rivers

Boats sail on the rivers,
And ships sail on the seas;
But clouds that sail across the sky
Are prettier far than these.

Christina Rossetti

Now you can make up another song of your own, both the words and the music. The rhymes of the poem will help you plan the phrase pattern of the tune.

The Chinese Vegetable Man

MAUDE S. KINNEY

CHINESE MELODY
popular in the PHILIPPINES and in HAWAII

The Chi-nese ped-dler trots a-long,

Chant-ing his mo-not-o-nous song,_____

Bal-anced bas-kets bob-bing up and down.

Trays are filled, Noth-ing spilled, Vege-ta-bles he's

ped-dling round the town, round the town.

PLAYING THE FLUTE

The flute is a straight, slender tube. The tone is produced by blowing across an opening near the end. Levers and keys are moved by the finger to make the different tones.

The music for the flute is written just as it is for the voice or the piano. The flute player can play the notes for the voice and be in tune with the singers.

The flute provides a silvery top to the music of both the band and the orchestra. The lowest tones are soft and rich like velvet. The upper tones are clear and bright like the call of a bird.

RANGE OF THE FLUTE

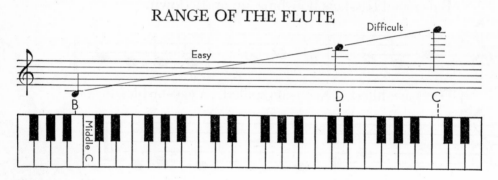

Someone who plays the flute can play this theme for you.

THEME
Dance of the Happy Spirits, from "Orpheus"

CHRISTOPH WILLIBALD VON GLUCK

Pipe and Drum Music from Mexico

People have always enjoyed listening to the pipes and drums.   Have you ever seen soldiers
marching to the music of the Fife and Drum Corps?
There are all kinds of musical pipes; tin whistles, flutes, recorders, clarinets, and many others.
Can you name some others?   You can make your own pipes out of hollow grass, bamboo,
dandelion stems, and twigs from willow trees.
The music on this page was used in a Mexican Indian ceremony.   The scale patterns, measures, and rhythms sound unusual and queer to us.

Rhythm of the Minuet

Slowly and with great dignity   See "Dance of the Happy Spirits"

The Laborers Out of Work

TRADITIONAL

Pray, Mas-ter, can— you— find for us Some— lit - tle job of work?

We'll hold the plow,—we'll—thresh the corn, And noth-ing will we shirk.

We've—wan-dered here, we've—wan-dered there, At—last we've come to you;

We are poor starv - ing— la - bor-ers, For— we've—no work to   do.

From *100 Singing Games, Old, New, and Adapted*, edited by Frank Kidson.
Reprinted by permission of Bayley & Ferguson, Glasgow.

One player is the farmer.   The rest are farm hands out of work.
Coming to the farmer, they sing the song given above.

(Spoken)   One of the farm hands: "Can you give us a job, mister?"
　　　　　Farmer:　　　　　　　"Well, what can you do?"
　　　　　Farm hand:　　　　　 "Anything, sir."
　　　　　Farmer:　　　　　　　"Well, let's see how *you* go about your work."

The farmer points to one of the farm hands, who pretends to do one kind of farm work.   This
　　may be milking, holding a plow, driving a horse, driving a tractor, sowing seed, or swinging a
　　scythe.   The farmer guesses what he is doing.   If the guess is correct, the farm hand is
　　hired.   He comes to the farmer's side of the room.   If the farmer's guess is wrong, the farm
　　hand goes to the other side of the room.
The rest of the farm hands repeat the song, and the game goes on until all the farm hands
　　have had their turn.   Then the two sides can have a tug-of-war.

Trees

W. Otto Miessner   W. Otto Miessner

(Boys) 1. The oak tree is stur - di - ly made,
(Girls) 2. The ma - ple is slen - der and tall,
(All) 3. The wil - low is grace - ful and thin,

I love him each year, more and more;
My fa - vor - ite tree, I con - fess;
Her dress is like sil - ver - y lace;

He fur - nish - es me pleas-ant shade
Her leaves are as gay in the Fall
She leans o'er the pool, gaz-ing in,

And nuts for the squir-rels to store.
As my love-ly cal - i - co dress.
Ad - mir - ing her beau - ti - ful face.

The Fountain

JAMES RUSSELL LOWELL

CLAYTON W. JOHNS

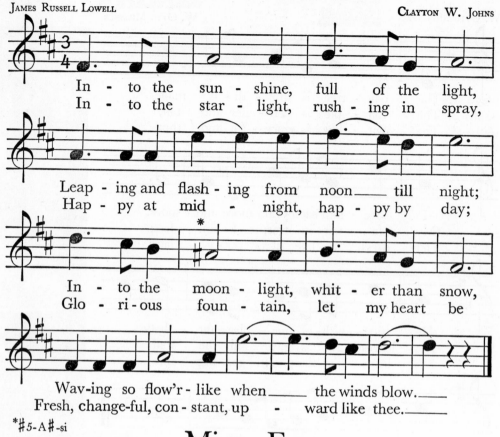

In - to the sun - shine, full of the light,
In - to the star - light, rush - ing in spray,

Leap - ing and flash - ing from noon___ till night;
Hap - py at mid - night, hap - py by day;

In - to the moon - light, whit - er than snow,
Glo - ri - ous foun - tain, let my heart be

Wav-ing so flow'r - like when___ the winds blow.___
Fresh, change-ful, con - stant, up - ward like thee.___

*♯5-A♯-si

Mister Fox

TRADITIONAL

ENGLISH FOLK SONG

1. A fox went out in a hun - gry plight, And he

begged of the moon to give him light, For he'd man - y miles to

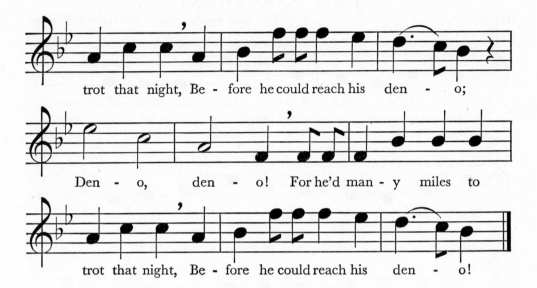

trot that night, Be - fore he could reach his den - o;

Den - o, den - o! For he'd man - y miles to

trot that night, Be - fore he could reach his den - o!

2. The fox, when he came to the farmer's stile,
   He lifted his ears and he listened a while;
   "Oho!" said the fox, "'Tis but a short mile
   From this to yonder town-o!"

3. The fox, he came to the farmer's gate,
   When whom should he see but the farmer's drake;
   "I love you well, for your master's sake,
   I long to be picking your bones-o!"

4. The gray goose came right round the haystack;
   "Oho!" said the fox, "You're very fat;
   You'll do very well to ride on my back
   From this to yonder den-o!"

5. Then old Mrs. Slipper-slopper jumped out of bed
   And out of the window she popped her head,
   "John, John, the old gray goose is gone
   And the fox is off to his den-o!"

6. The farmer loaded his pistol with lead
   And he shot the old fox right through the head;
   "Aha!" said the farmer, "You're now quite dead
   And no more you'll trouble the town-o!"

Jolly Old Roger

TRADITIONAL

FOLK SONG from the GREEN MOUNTAINS OF VERMONT

1. 'Twas jol - ly old Rog - er, the tin - mak - er's man,
2. His pipe was a meer-schaum of pot - ter - y clay;
3. But jol - ly old Rog - er had two pairs of eyes;

Who lived in a gar - ret in New Am - ster - dam,
He smoked it and col - ored it man - y a day.
His glass - es, called "specs," were un - com - mon in size;

Who show - ered down bless - ings like rain in the spring
He had but one leg and he wore but one shoe,
His nose like a straw - ber - ry, rac - y and red,

On maid - ens and ma - trons. Oh, him I would sing!
And stumped round his shop on a stiff tim - ber toe.
A "snuff - er" by day and a trum - pet in bed.

CHORUS

There nev - er was yet a boy or a man Who

bet - ter could tink - er a ket - tle or pan, Or buck - et, or

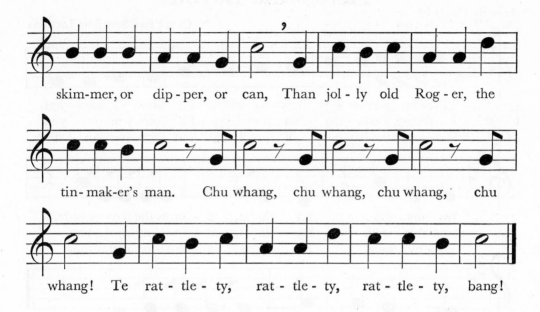

skim-mer, or dip-per, or can, Than jol-ly old Rog-er, the

tin-mak-er's man. Chu whang, chu whang, chu whang, chu

whang! Te rat-tle-ty, rat-tle-ty, rat-tle-ty, bang!

The Birthday

Lei (pronounced lā-ē), is the flower garland so characteristic of Hawaii.

BERTA METZGER

HAWAIIAN SONG by
CHARLES KING

Weave a lei,_____ my birth-day is to-day!_____

Chant and sing,_____ While we dance and sway._____

Voice study. Sing this song with "la" and "oh," and hold the long tones with fine quality to the very end.

Across the Bayou

From the CREOLE by
ALICE WHITSON NORTON

CREOLE FOLK SONG from LOUISIANA

(Boys) 1. Lit-tle lass, a-cross the bay- ou wide, I'd like to have you
(Girls) 2. Lit-tle lad, a-row - ing on the bay, I'll join you if you
(All) 3. Float-ing on the bay-ou all day long, And join - ing in a

by my side. La la la, a - cross the bay-ou wide,
come this way. La la la, a - row-ing on the bay,
hap - py song. La la la, a - float-ing all day long,

La la la, a - sit-ting by my side.
La la la, I wish you'd come this way.
La la la, and join-ing in a song.

The Little White Lamb
(L'Agneau, la Neige, et le Lait)

Paraphrased from the FRENCH of
SUZANNE CHAINAYE by
JANE ROLFE RANDOLPH

CHILDREN'S SONG from BELGIUM by
FRANCIS DE BOURGUIGNON

1. Once a lit - tle lamb looked in - to a pool,
1. Le pe - tit mou - ton dans la plai - ne,

Proud in - deed was he at the sight,
Dis - ait d'un air fier et con - tent,

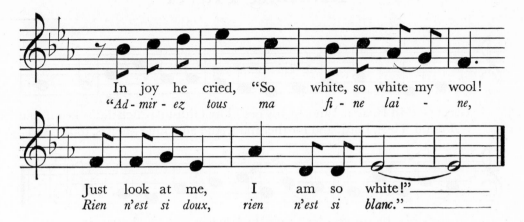

In joy he cried, "So white, so white my wool!
"Ad - mir - ez tous ma fi - ne lai - ne,

Just look at me, I am so white!"_____
Rien n'est si doux, rien n'est si blanc."_____

2. "Lambkin," said the milk, speaking from the pail,
   Boasting is not good, little lamb."
   He baaed again and proudly shook his tail,
   "Just look at me, how white I am!"

3. Then the snow began, lightly fluttering,
   Drifting, drifting down, beautiful
   Upon each bush, and over everything
   And on the proud lamb's curly wool.

4. Quickly cried the milk, "Ah, my little one,
   Lambs are rather white, it is true,
   But you will learn, dear lamb, before you're done
   There're many things whiter than you!"

2. *Il tourmentait fort de la sorte*
   Le lait — moins blanc — dans son bol bleu:
   "Ah! mais vraiment, il m'insupporte,"
   Disait le lait, "Quel vaniteux!"

3. *Soudain voici la neige blanche*
   Qui tombe, tombe en clairs flocons.
   Ils sont — regarde sur la branche —
   Dix fois plus blancs que les moutons!

4. *Et le lait dit en sa cachette:*
   "Mon bel agneau, si blanc qu'on soit,
   Il faut se mettre dans la tête
   Qu'il est toujours plus blanc que soi!"

Morning Prayer

CARL REINECKE

Great God in Heav'n, Who, by my bed, Thy faith-ful watch did'st keep; And
I thank Thee, Lord, and Fa-ther mild, And all Thine an-gels, too,   And

night's_best bless-ings o'er__ me shed, Sweet rest, and balm - y   sleep.
pray__Thee still to   help__Thy child Thy ho - ly will   to   do.

Every Night

ELSIE J. COOLEY

MYLES BIRKET FOSTER

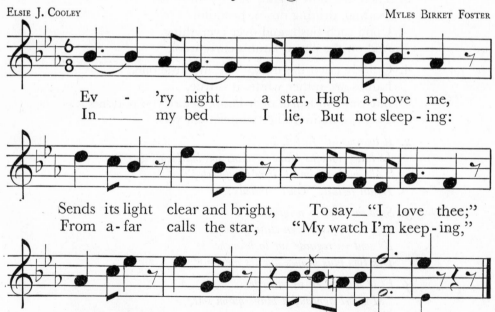

Ev - 'ry night____ a star, High a-bove me,
In____ my bed____ I lie, But not sleep - ing:

Sends its light   clear and bright,   To say__"I love thee;"
From a - far   calls the star,   "My watch I'm keep - ing,"

Sends its light, clear and bright,   To say__"I love   thee."
From a-far   calls the star,   "My watch I'm keep-ing."

I Plant Some Rice

The action song is very popular among the Ilocano peoples in the Philippines.

The action takes place on the first beat of measures 1, 2, 6, and 7. In the first verse the rice is planted. In verse 2 the rice is harvested with a little cutting instrument like a pruning-shears (not a scythe or sickle). In verses 3, 4, and 5, the words *pound*, *cook*, and *eat* may likewise be dramatized.

ACTION SONG

PHILIPPINE FOLK SONG from ILOCOS SUR
Notation by FLORENCIO BUADO

1. I plant some rice, I plant some rice,
2. I har-vest rice, I har-vest rice,

Tra la la la la la.
Tra la la la la la.

I plant some rice, I plant some rice,
I har-vest rice, I har-vest rice,

And that's a job well done.
And that's a job well done

3. I pound some rice.
4. I cook some rice.
5. I eat some rice.

Bright Fire in Your Eyes
(Cueca)

FOLK SONG from CHILE

Bright fire in your eyes   is flam-ing,_____ Like cor - als, your
Tus o - jos son vi - va lla - ma,_____ Tu bo - ca fi-

lips   are ros - y,_____ And when you smile, pearls are gleam-ing,_____
no   co - ral,_____ Tu son - ri - sa os-ten - ta per-las,

Most pre-cious of all   the   sea._____ all   the   sea._____
Las más pre - cio - sas   del   mar._____ sas   del   mar._____

Sharp-2 in the Key of G

A#

G A B C D E (F#) G

3 #2 3
B A# B
mi ri mi

Sharp-4 in the Key of G

C#

G A B C D E (F#) G

5 #4 5
D C# D
so fi so

The Old Gavotte

VIRGINIA C. MURDOCK   W. OTTO MIESSNER

Rain - y   days, in-to Grand-ma's at-tic go - ing, Trunks we

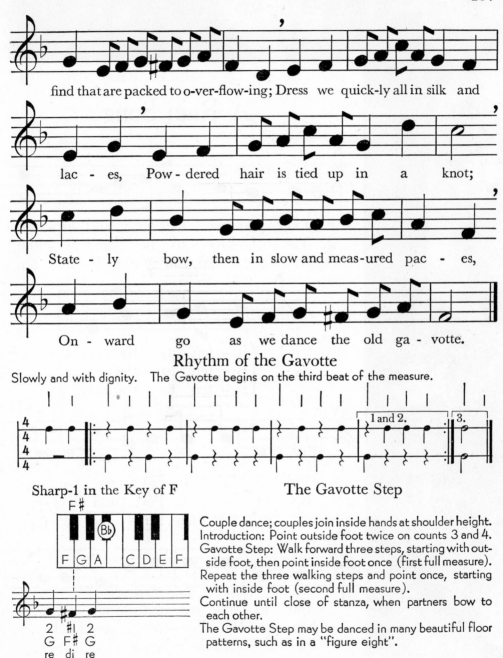

find that are packed to o-ver-flow-ing; Dress we quick-ly all in silk and

lac - es, Pow - dered hair is tied up in a knot;

State - ly bow, then in slow and meas-ured pac - es,

On - ward go as we dance the old ga - votte.

Rhythm of the Gavotte

Slowly and with dignity. The Gavotte begins on the third beat of the measure.

1 and 2.   3.

Sharp-1 in the Key of F

F♯

F G A   C D E F

2 ♯1 2
G F♯ G
re di re

The Gavotte Step

Couple dance; couples join inside hands at shoulder height.
Introduction: Point outside foot twice on counts 3 and 4.
Gavotte Step: Walk forward three steps, starting with out-
side foot, then point inside foot once (first full measure).
Repeat the three walking steps and point once, starting
with inside foot (second full measure).
Continue until close of stanza, when partners bow to
each other.
The Gavotte Step may be danced in many beautiful floor
patterns, such as in a "figure eight".

A Rain Song

CLINTON SCOLLARD   PAUL HINDEMITH

1. Don't you love to lie— and lis - ten,
2. Yes, I love to lie— and lis - ten,
3. That's my dream, the while— I lis - ten,

Lis - ten to the rain,
Lis - ten to the rain.
Lis - ten to the rain.

With its lit - tle pat - ter, pat-ter,
It's the fair - ies, Pert— and Pluck-y,
I can see them, run - ning rac - es,

And its ti - ny clat - ter, clat-ter,
Nip, and Nim - ble - toes,— and Luck-y,
I can watch their laugh - ing fac-es,

158

And its sil - v'ry spat - ter, spat-ter,
Trip, and Thim-ble -nose,_ and Tuck-y,
At their glee - ful games and grac-es,

On the roof_____
On the roof_____
On the roof_____

And on the pane?
And on the pane.
And on the pane!

159

Music

ROBERT LOUIS STEVENSON

EDWARD BAILEY BIRGE

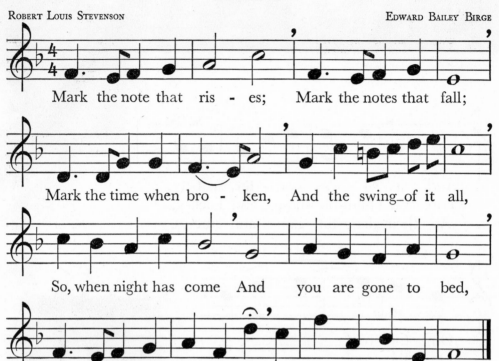

Mark the note that ris - es; Mark the notes that fall;

Mark the time when bro - ken, And the swing of it all,

So, when night has come And you are gone to bed,

All the songs you love to sing Will ech - o in your head.

All Around There's Beauty

MARTHA DABNEY

CHILDREN'S SONG from FINLAND by MARTTI TURUNEN

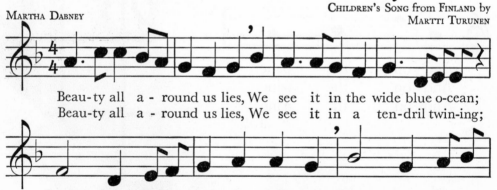

Beau-ty all a - round us lies, We see it in the wide blue o-cean;
Beau-ty all a - round us lies, We see it in a ten-dril twin-ing;

Sweet, clear, when a bird is call - ing, Slow, near, when a
Bright, bright when the hearth is glow - ing, Soft, light, when the

leaf is fall - ing, Fair in shad-ow's love-ly___ mo - tion.
dawn is show-ing; Ev - 'ry-where is beau-ty___ shin - ing.

Ris, Ras

Paraphrased from the SPANISH by
MARTHA DABNEY

SPANISH AMERICAN FOLK SONG

The car-pen-ters are saw - ing, Saw - dust is fly - ing,
The car-pen-ters are plan - ing, Boys come and watch them;

And round their feet the piec - es Thick - ly are ly - ing;
They want the curl - y shav - ings, Gai - ly they catch them;

Saw goes "Ris," (Imitate sound of saw) Saw goes "Ras," (Imitate)
Plane goes "Ris," (" " "plane) Plane goes "Ras," (")

The car-pen-ters are saw - ing, Saw - ing all day.
The car-pen-ters keep plan - ing, Plan - ing a - way.

You can step to this song while clapping the note patterns.

The Keeper

TRADITIONAL

OLD ENGLISH SONG

1. The keep-er did a-shoot-ing go, And
2. The first doe he shot at he missed; The

un-der his cloak he car-ried a bow,___All for to shoot at a
sec - ond doe he trimmed he kissed; The third doe___went where___

mer-ry lit-tle doe A - mong the leaves so___green, O.
no - bod-y wist A - mong the leaves so___green, O.

Jack-ie, boy! Sing ye well! Hey down, der-ry, der-ry down,

Mas-ter! Ver-y well! Ho down,

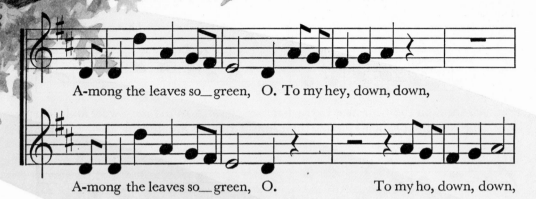

A-mong the leaves so__green, O. To my hey, down, down,

A-mong the leaves so__green, O.   To my ho, down, down,

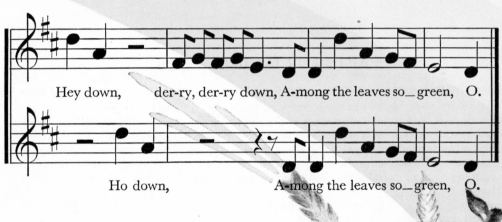

Hey down,   der-ry, der-ry down, A-mong the leaves so__green, O.

Ho down,   A-mong the leaves so__green, O.

3. The fourth doe she did cross the plain,
   The keeper fetched her back again;
   Where she is now she may remain
   Among the leaves so green, O.

4. The fifth doe she did cross the brook;
   The keeper fetched her back with his crook;
   Where she is now you must go and look
   Among the leaves so green, O.

5. The sixth doe she ran over the plain;
   But he with his hounds did turn her again,
   And it's there he did hunt in a merry, merry vein
   Among the leaves so green, O.

Music Everywhere

Translated by
VIRGINIA HARRISON

BAVARIAN FOLK SONG

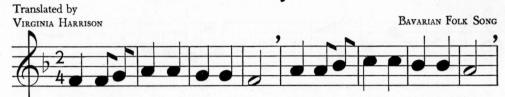

All through the sum-mer I can hear Songs all a-round me, sweet and clear;
Birds in the branch-es make their song, Crick-ets are flut-ing all day long;

Bees in clo-ver-lands hum-ming low, Brook-lets sing-ing as they flow.
Mu - sic all a-round, far and near, When I lis-ten, I can hear.

PARTS FOR INSTRUMENTS

MUSIC EVERYWHERE is in the key of F. Parts for several instruments are given. How many instruments would you need to play all the music on these two pages?

The violin and flute use the same notes as the singers. The music for the clarinet in B-flat and the cornet in B-flat is written one whole-step higher, in the key of G. Yet the tones of the clarinet and the cornet sound the same as the tones of the singers and the other instruments. The music for the drums does not require a staff, although drum parts often are written on a staff. The piano plays other parts as well as the melody. That gives us the harmony.

Any or all of these instrumental parts may be played to accompany the singers. They may also be played as an instrumental selection.

Many of the other songs in the book can be arranged for instruments.

You might ask people who play these instruments to play with you while you sing this song.

Music Everywhere

BAVARIAN FOLK SONG

Violin and Flute

Music Everywhere

Music Everywhere

Music Everywhere

Little Dutch Mina

MARTHA DABNEY

DUTCH FOLK DANCE

O - ver in Hol - land where tu - lips are gay,
By the ca - nal, with a clack - e - ty sound,

Lit - tle Dutch Mi - na goes danc - ing a - way,
See the broad arms of the wind - mill turn round;

In her big wood - en shoes waltz - ing a - long,
Lit - tle Dutch Mi - na goes cheer - y and bright;

Sing - ing a rol - lick - ing, frol - ick - ing song.
Shoes may be heav - y, but hearts can be light.

The small notes may be played by an accompanying instrument.
Wooden Shoe Waltz: Step on the right foot to the right; brush the left foot forward; hop on the right foot (one measure). Repeat, beginning with the left foot.

The Bird's Nest

John Drinkwater

Mary Howe

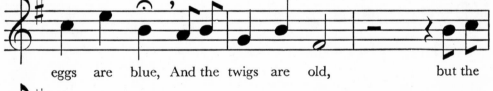

I know a place, in the i-vy on a tree, Where a

bird's nest is, and the eggs are three; And the bird is brown, and the

eggs are blue, And the twigs are old, but the

moss is new; And I go quite near, though I

think I should have heard The sound of me watch-ing, if I had been a bird.

167

Brothers, Row

JEAN JACQUES ROUSSEAU
with DESCANT by LOWELL MASON

O'er the wa-ter gen-tly float-ing, Hear the boat-men cheer-ful sing-ing,

Broth - ers,___ row, we're home re - turn - ing,

Fine

Home re-turn-ing from their la - bor, Sing-ing as they row.

Joy - ful___ greet - ing waits us there.

La - bor end-ed, rest be-fore them, Sweet to them the hour of eve-ning;

Bright our___ hearth - fires now are burn - ing,

Lov-ing hearts at home a-wait them, Well the wea-ry boat-men know. Then

Fac - es__ loved a wel - come wear.

D.C. al Fine means to go back to the beginning and continue to the place marked *Fine*, a word meaning *the end*.

Chanticleer

John Farrar

Clare E. Grundman

1. High and proud on the barn-yard fence Walks roost-er in the
up, you la - zy__ boys and girls, It's time you should be

morn - ing; He shakes his comb, he shakes his tail, And
dress - ing!" I won - der if he keeps a clock, Or

gives his dai - ly warn - ing. 2. "Get
if he's on - ly guess - ing.

Twilight on the Farm

HARRIET WARE   HARRIET WARE

The warm milk foams up in the pail,

And some-times it spills o - ver.

The kind old cow stands qui - et - ly;

She smells of hay and clo - ver.

170

I hold my cup and drink the milk

And thus to bed by can - dle-light.

I hear the bird - ies say their prayers.

Dear love - ly farm, good night, good night.

Pas bien grand

From the FRENCH of JACQUELINE KRIEGER
by CYNTHIA STEWART

Not So Big

CHILDREN'S SONG from FRANCE by
DARIUS MILHAUD

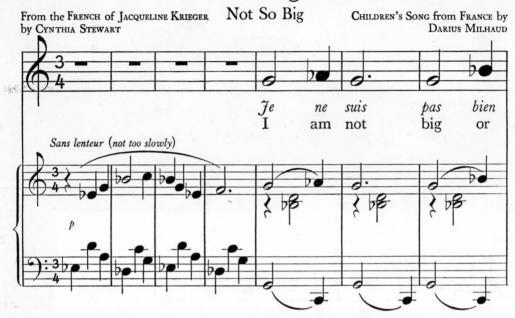

Je   ne   suis   pas   bien
I   am   not   big   or

Sans lenteur (not too slowly)

p

grand   Car   je   n'ai   que   neuf   ans,
strong   For   I   am   on-ly   nine,

Mais   pour pe - ti - te   mè - - re   Je
But   my   dear lit - tle moth - - er Would

suis   tout l'u - ni - vers.
say   I'm ver - y fine.

The Measure Rest (▬) occurs six times in this song.   The time signature tells us that for
each measure rest the voices do not sing for three beats.

The FARANDOLE is an old dance from the south of France. It is something like playing "follow the leader." The dancers form a chain, holding one another by the hands or by ribbons or handkerchiefs. The leader holds the next dancer with his left hand, while with his right hand he waves a flag or ribbon. A little band of flutes and drums provides the accompaniment. The leader makes the line come and go, twist and turn, form a ring or a spiral. As the dancers move about they are constantly joined by others. The dance usually ends with the leader guiding the line into some kind of floor pattern. The Farandole can also be danced to WILD DUCK FEATHERS FALLING, page 72.

The Farandole

Nancy Byrd Turner

Georges Bizet
from "L'Arlésienne"

Oh, come and fol-low, ev-'ry-one, Oh, come and fol-low, sing - ing!
And when his rib-bon flut-ters high, Or when it's back-ward swing-ing,

Our lead-er leads us gai - ly on, We watch him for a sign;
All hand in hand and mer-ri - ly We fol-low in a

line. Then dance a-long, one! And dance a-long, all!

The tune is beat-ing time for us, We'll an-swer to the call!

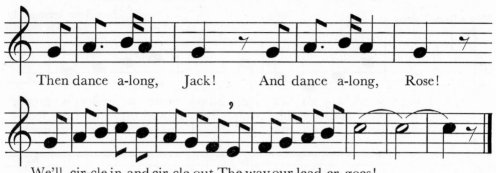

Then dance a-long, Jack! And dance a-long, Rose!

We'll cir-cle in and cir-cle out The way our lead-er goes!___

The Summer Wind

L. H. BAILEY

FRANCIS H. McKAY

The wind, ___ the wind, ___ the gen - tle sum - mer wind, ___

In i-dle ease___ through weeds and trees it wafts and woos and soothes me

And I fall___ a - sleep ___ right where the grass ___ is deep, ___

In the warm, gen - tle sum - mer wind. ___

The Little Maid at the Inn

Nancy Byrd Turner

Folk Song arranged by
Johannes Brahms

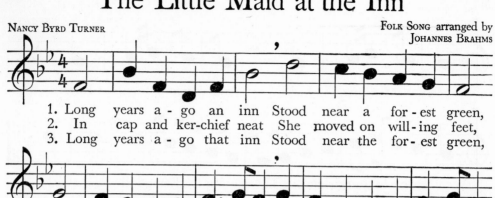

1. Long years a - go an inn Stood near a for - est green,
2. In cap and ker-chief neat She moved on will - ing feet,
3. Long years a - go that inn Stood near the for - est green,

And there a blue-eyed lit-tle maid Would serve the hon-ey and the bread,
With so much sun-light in her face She made the room a pleas-ant place,
Long years a - go, yet e - ven now We hear a-bout its cheer, and how

And keep the win-dows all a-light With can-dles burn-ing bright.
And ev-'ry guest would stay a-while To watch her mer - ry smile.
One lit - tle maid so trim and fair Gave hap - py wel-come there.

Praise to God, Immortal Praise

A. L. Barbauld

Chorale

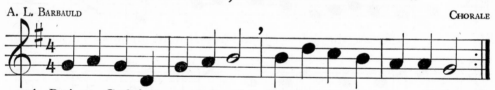

1. Praise to God, im - mor-tal praise, For the love that crowns our days;
   Boun-teous source of ev - 'ry joy, Let Thy praise our tongues em-ploy;

2. As Thy pros-p'ring hand hath blest May we give Thee of our best;
   And by deeds of kind-ly love For Thy mer-cies grate-ful prove;

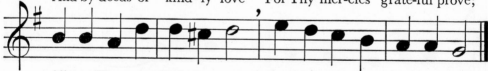

All to Thee, our God, we owe, Source whence all our bless-ings flow.
Sing-ing thus through all our days, Praise to God, im - mor-tal praise.

Echo

Kate Cox Goddard

W. Otto Miessner

I stood up-on a moun-tain one fine day, Yoo-

Echo (may be sung or played)

Yoo-hoo!

hoo! I saw an-oth-er moun-tain, oh, so high It

blue sky

near-ly touched the bright blue sky, Yoo-

Yoo-hoo! Yoo-hoo! Yoo-hoo!

hoo, Yoo-hoo, Yoo-hoo!

The Birds' Conversation

TRADITIONAL FOLK SONG from KENTUCKY

1. "Well," said the black-bird to the crow, "What makes the farm-er
2. "Well," said the owl with his head so big, "Once I ate a
3. "Well," said the par-tridge sit-ting in a thick-et, "I wish I had a
4. "Well," said the wood-peck-er sit-ting in the grass, "Once I court-ed a

hate us so?" "Be-cause, ev-er since old Ad-am was made,
roast-ed pig, But now I have to sit up-on a stake And
yel-low jack-et, I'd pull off yel-low and put on green, And
bon-ny lass; She proved fick-le and from me fled,

Pull-ing up corn has been our trade."
eat a piece of cold fro-zen snake."
then I would sit up for a queen."
Ev-er since then my head's been red."

THE HUNGARIAN GYPSIES DANCE FOR BRAHMS

Theme: HUNGARIAN DANCE No. 5 — BRAHMS

Theme: HUNGARIAN DANCE No. 6 — BRAHMS

FARANDOLE, from "L'ARLÉSIENNE" SUITE — BIZET. See song on page 174.

America

Samuel Francis Smith

Henry Carey

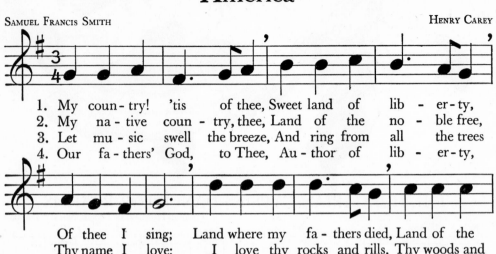

1. My coun-try! 'tis of thee, Sweet land of lib - er-ty,
2. My na - tive coun - try, thee, Land of the no - ble free,
3. Let mu - sic swell the breeze, And ring from all the trees
4. Our fa - thers' God, to Thee, Au - thor of lib - er-ty,

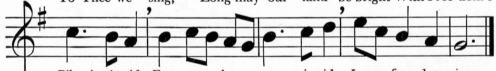

Of thee I sing; Land where my fa - thers died, Land of the
Thy name I love; I love thy rocks and rills, Thy woods and
Sweet Free-dom's song; Let mor - tal tongues a-wake, Let all that
To Thee we sing; Long may our land be bright With Free-dom's

Pil-grims' pride, From ev - 'ry moun-tain side Let free-dom ring.
tem - pled hills, My heart with rap-ture thrills Like that a - bove.
breathe par-take, Let rocks their si - lence break, The sound pro-long.
ho - ly light; Pro-tect us by Thy might, Great God, our King.

USING THE FOURTH BOOK IN THE CLASSROOM

In the primary grades NEW MUSIC HORIZONS helps the children to find in music a happy means of aesthetic and emotional self-expression. This is achieved through a five-fold program of music activities and experiences: Singing, Playing, Dancing, Listening, and Creating. These activities also constitute a "reading readiness" program, which is briefly outlined in the teachers' helps at the back of the Second and Third Books. The primary grades thus become a period of enrichment out of which a readiness for the development of further and more specific skills should emerge.

In the intermediate grades the acquirement of these skills becomes a definite objective of the music activities. Increasing ability to use the musical score is an important aim in these years. In the primary grades the score is essentially a record of songs learned by rote. In the intermediate grades the score becomes a means for new musical experiences. The Fourth, Fifth, and Sixth Books carry forward through progressive steps the continuing and expanding five-fold program of music activities. All pupils are exposed to these varied experiences, each child discovering those phases to which he responds most favorably and which, in time, may become his own happiest self-expression.

In the lower grades the picture establishes the mood of the song and enables the child to create his own interpretative expression. In the intermediate grades pictures build upon this background. They locate the song in place and time, and thereby contribute to the social program. Above all, the illustrations in NEW MUSIC HORIZONS appeal to the sense of beauty, which is a primary aim of instruction in all the arts.

The following outline is a condensation of the complete directions to be found in the teacher's book.

I. MUSIC READING

The program of reading readiness in the primary grades has made the pupils conscious of tone as high and low, rising and falling, long and short, quick and slow, loud and soft. In the Second Book the ear led in recognizing these elements; in the Third Book the eye observed the way they were expressed in music notation. The child's observation has been both general and specific. He has experienced, studied, and utilized the fundamental elements of music and of music notation, such as songs in a number of keys, the phrase, tonal and rhythmic groups or patterns, the beat, accent, and measure groups. The Fourth Book carries forward a music reading program in which skill in the use of music notation is acquired. The program approaches the subject with such simplicity, variety, and appeal that every pupil can be expected to find in it a high degree of pleasure and success.

A. *Phrase Patterns.* Recognition of phrases that are alike, similar, and different contributes directly to facility in music reading, taking it out of the realm of note-to-note calling and into the field of reading by musical thoughts. The association of this experience with both the music reading and the creative programs helps to develop the conception of music as a language which communicates tonal ideas. See pp. 4, 7a, 7b, 71, 80b, 116, 117, 128a, 142. Many songs in the Fourth Book should be taught by rote, with pupils following the music notation from their books. Rote songs may be taught phrase-wise or by the whole-song method.

B. *Tonal.* The music reading program includes the familiar practices of using the so-fa syllables, scale numbers, and pitch names, as preferred by the teacher. In addition to these devices, the Fourth Book offers a plan in which the piano keyboard (or a keyboard diagram), bells, and simple wind instruments provide a functional means for the study of pitch relations within an easily understood "space-frame."

1. Songs in five keys. In the primary grades the children learned that songs may appear in many keys, and thought in terms of the tones as related to any given keynote. The rote songs in the Fourth Book appear in many keys. In the music reading program of the intermediate grades the keys are presented for study one at a time, (a) to fix positively the key location in a limited number of keys; (b) to give material enough in each key to establish reading habits; and (c) to correlate with the instrumental program wherein manipulation of the instrument aids in fixing a definite knowledge of tonal relationships within the given scale and also as absolute pitches.

a. Key of C—Keyboard Chart, p. 6. Songs on pp. 7, 10, 11, 14b, 15, 34b, 38, 39, 46

b. Key of C, tones in the upper scale—Keyboard Chart, p. 22. Songs on pp. 23, 26, 31, 34a, 35

c. Key of G—Keyboard Chart, p. 42. Songs on pp. 43, 45, 47, 50, 51, 54, 55, 58, 77b

d. Key of D—Keyboard Chart, p. 62. Songs on pp. 63, 64, 66, 67, 70, 75, 77a, 97

e. Key of F—Keyboard Chart, p. 82. Songs on pp. 83, 84, 85, 88b, 89, 91, 95

f. Key of B-flat—Keyboard Chart, p. 104. Songs on pp. 105, 108, 116, 117, 118a, 148b, 176a

2. **Part Singing, preparatory.** Good part singing involves the ability to think tonal combinations. The following songs offer opportunities for such experience, presented with the utmost simplicity and in the spirit of fun: pp. 62, 83b, 84b, 115, 118a, 120, 121a, 122, 156, 162, 168, 177.

3. **Sharp Chromatics, diatonic (scalewise) half-steps.** Just as the tonal relations within the five keys studied in the Fourth Book become clear by reference to the keyboard space-frame, so this simplest form of chromatics is presented and clarified by a similar procedure. See pp. 136, 137, 148a, 150, 155, 156a, 156b, 176b.

C. *Rhythmic.* The reading readiness program of the primary grades includes much experience in physical activities related to and expressing musical rhythms. These are continued and expanded in the Fourth Book and applied specifically to the development of skill in music reading.

1. **Keeping time.** Scansion of the poetic text may be employed along with other more specific forms of drill. The use of the strokes (a simple down beat with the forearm, taken from the practice so popular and successful in the Elizabethan days of universal madrigal singing) is a most practical device for mastering the elements of time keeping. The strokes are indicated in connection with the drum music throughout the book. The use of drum notation, continued from the primary grades, offers an interesting and entertaining, as well as a highly practical, means for clarifying the beat, accent, measure, rhythmic patterns, and their notation.

a. Beat, accent, measure: pp. 3, 10, 15, 27, 66

b. Time signature: pp. 3 (4/4), 15 (2/4), 27 (3/4)

c. Note values: pp. 3, 66, 128, 129, 160

d. The rest: pp. 14, 38 (Quarter Rest); p. 23 (Half Rest); pp. 100, 172 (Measure Rest)

e. The hold: pp. 34a, 45, 49, 84a, 154a

f. The tie, the slur: pp. 51, 85, 95, 132b

g. Eighth notes, separated: pp. 66, 67a, 67b, 70, 75, 77a, 77b, 88a, 95, 100

h. Eighth notes with ties, crossbeams, slurs: pp. 66, 86a, 86b, 87, 88b, 91, 92, 95, 98, 101, 130, 131

i. Dotted quarter and eighth notes: pp. 128a, 128b, 129, 132a, 132b, 135a, 135b, 139, 140b, 143, 148a, 148b, 151, 152, 154a, 160b, 164, 166, 170, 176a, 180

2. **Dance rhythms.** Certain of the more familiar and simpler dance rhythms, which are basic in instrumental forms, unify the activities of the dance program, the instrumental program, and the music reading program.

a. Marching: p. 10

b. Waltz: pp. 26, 27, 31, 38, 39, 108, 166

c. Polka: p. 97

d. Schottische: p. 106

e. Mazurka: p. 133

f. Minuet: p. 145

g. Gavotte: p. 156

h. Farandole: p. 174

3. **Stepping-Clapping.** This activity is of the highest value in bringing into play the kinesthetic (muscle) sense as a basic experience in developing the feeling for rhythm and time and the mastery of their notation. The continuous forward movement of music is maintained by stepping the beats or dance rhythms with the large, propulsive muscles of the legs. At the same time, by clapping the note patterns with the finer muscles of the arms and wrists, a balance is secured between the feeling for the swing of the music and its rhythmic details. See pp. 3, 7a, 7b, 10, 15, 26, 27, 31, 38, 54a, 57, 66, 67a, 67b, 70, 97, 100, 106, 108, 133, 156, 161.

II. EXPRESSIVE SINGING

In the Fourth Book the singing program falls under three headings:

1. **Voice Compass.** The songs have been selected and the keys chosen with careful attention to the use of the child voice of fourth grade level.

2. **Tonal Memory.** The use of musical figures from songs in the book is suggested for testing and developing tonal memory. This is a further development of the idea of "Tone Matching" suggested in the Second Book and the Third Book. Children should remember and be able to sing such figures accurately in higher and lower keys. Songs with figures appropriate for this use are found on pp. 4, 26, 78, 81, 84, 105, 115, 154b, 170.

3. **Tone Quality.**

a. More and more each year children should be made conscious of the importance of singing with beautiful tone quality, in order to express the moods and meanings of the songs in their books. This should be kept in mind at all times, but certain songs have been selected for particular study and thought. These will be found on pp. 14, 23, 43b, 108, 131, 137, 140a, 151.

b. Occasionally the teacher should hear the boys and girls sing songs separately. The pupils may indicate their own choice of these songs. On p. 147 and p. 152 songs are given with certain stanzas for the boys to sing, and certain stanzas for the girls to sing. On p. 168 the boys may sing the rowing song and the girls may sing the descant. A fine spirit of competition between the boys and girls may be developed in this way, which will aid in securing good singing. Other songs appropriate for this use are:

(1) Songs for boys: pp. 8, 32, 60, 65, 85, 95, 125, 132, 139, 150

(2) Songs for girls: pp. 4, 14, 76, 78, 108, 112, 123, 141, 154, 170

III. PLAYING AN INSTRUMENT

Instrumental music is recognized today as a basic part of music education. The instrumental program in NEW MUSIC HORIZONS does not include instruction in the techniques of playing. In the Fourth Book the instrumental program is designed to (a) provide all pupils with a minimum background of information concerning certain of the most important musical instruments; (b) encourage children to take up the study of some instrument; (c) utilize playing on percussion instruments in the expanded programs of music reading, dancing, and listening; (d) socialize the whole music program by encouraging each child to participate in the general ensemble in the way that he will enjoy most and to the degree that he will profit most.

A. Drum Music. Where actual instruments are not available, tapping with the finger tips for the small drum, and beating the palm of the left hand with a wide motion of the right fist for the big drum, will meet all essential requirements.

1. Keeping time: pp. 3, 15, 27, 145
2. Dance rhythms: pp. 10, 27, 97, 106, 133, 145, 156
3. Other percussion instruments: p. 100 (tambourine); p. 108 (triangle)

B. Bells, Piano (Keyboard space-frame). If all of the songs in the music reading program were played by all pupils on one of the keyboard space-frame instruments, problems of music reading would be reduced to a minimum. This activity is relatively simple and easy, and is both inviting and entertaining. See pp. 6, 7, 22, 42, 46, 62, 82, 104, 136, 137, 156, 157, 165.

C. Pipes, Whistles, and Recorders. The widespread use of these instruments, both for enjoyment and as an introduction to instrumental performance, should be further encouraged. Their use should also be a definite part of the music reading program. See pp. 6, 22, 30, 31, 145.

D. Instruments of the orchestra and band. These lessons are designed to awaken an interest in instrumental performance. Pupils from the upper grades may be invited to demonstrate for the younger pupils and may play along with the singers as a beginning of socialized vocal and instrumental ensembles.

1. Violin: pp. 74, 75, 164
2. Clarinet: pp. 90, 91, 96, 165
3. Cornet (Trumpet): pp. 124, 125, 165
4. Flute: pp. 144, 145, 164

E. The Instrumental Score. Beginning with the simple scoring of small and big drums, the pupils are introduced to the way music scoring is arranged and instrumental parts are written. See pp. 79, 164, 165.

IV. RHYTHMIC ACTIVITIES

An outline of the rhythmic activities suggested by NEW MUSIC HORIZONS for the primary grades would include: (a) Fundamental movements of legs, arms, and trunk, such as walking, marching, running, skipping, hopping, swaying, swinging, bending, etc.; (b) Impersonation, pretending, pantomime, dramatization; (c) Dance steps—polka step, waltz step, gavotte, and schottische step; (d) Singing games and singing folk dances. Through these experiences the children are helped to develop a feeling for rhythm and accent. They learn to keep step and to move in unison with music, to achieve poise, self-control, and grace of movement. They acquire also a vocabulary of movements which expand their own powers of creative physical self-expression in dance, dramatics, and pageantry.

In the intermediate grades all of these activities are continued, stepped-up to this higher level. Furthermore, these experiences become directly and consciously related to rhythms, meters, phrasing, and time keeping in the music reading program, both vocal and instrumental; to interpretation in the singing program; to the music appreciation and listening program; and to the feeling for rhythm and structure in melodic invention, as well as the continuance of dramatics and pageantry, in the creative program.

A. Fundamental Movements:
1. Marching: p. 10, and other songs under "Marching" in the list of Social Dances.
2. Swinging: pp. 7a, 126
3. Swaying: pp. 14, 43a
4. Skipping: pp. 57, 134
5. Lumbering walk: p. 110

B. Singing Games:
pp. 2, 50, 58, 86a, 87, 88a, 89, 102, 109, 120, 121b, 146, 155

C. Folk Dances:
pp. 16, 72, 80, 81, 166, 174

D. Social Dances:
1. Marching: pp. 5, 10, 35, 65, 79, 96, 100, 125, 161, 174
2. Waltz Walk: pp. 26, 27, 31
3. Waltz Step: pp. 38, 39, 50, 70, 75, 108, 156
4. Minuet: pp. 90, 144, 145
5. Polka: p. 97
6. Schottische: p. 106
7. Mazurka: p. 133
8. Gavotte: p. 156
9. Wooden Shoe Waltz: p. 166

V. LISTENING

"Hearing is the very center of musicianship." Therefore the essential basis of any program of music instruction must be the development of skillful listening, or "ear training." This is true from the first rote song to the most advanced levels of study and experience.

A. Throughout NEW MUSIC HORIZONS definite emphasis is given to that field of listening generally termed "music appreciation." Special pages in the Fourth Book are devoted to this phase of the listening program. Themes are given from important compositions associated with the other fields of the five-fold activities program.

p. 12 *Three Kinds of Marches*
Theme: Triumphal March, from "Sigurd Jorsalfar"—Grieg
Theme: Turkish March, from "The Ruins of Athens"—Beethoven
Theme: March, Semper Fideles—Sousa

p. 29 *Fairy Tales in Music*
Theme: Dance of the Toy Flutes, from "The Nutcracker" Suite—Tschaikowsky
Theme: Waltz, from "The Sleeping Beauty"—Tschaikowsky
Theme: Waltz, Roses from the South—Strauss. See song on page 108.

p. 52 *Two Master Composers*
Theme: Prelude in A-Major—Chopin
Theme: Air, from Suite No. 3 in D—Bach Arranged for violin G-string by August Wilhelmj

p. 68 *Mexico and Arabia in Music*
Theme: La Golondrina (The Swallow)—Serradell
Theme: Anitra's Dance, from "Peer Gynt" Suite—Grieg

p. 94 *Ceremonial and Ballroom Dances*
Theme: War Dance, from "Two Indian Dances"—Skilton
Theme: Intermezzo, from "Fairy Tales"—Suk
Theme: Menuet, from Symphony in E-Flat —Mozart. See Theme on page 90.

p. 119 *Day Music and Night Music*
Theme: Gondoliers, from "A Day in Venice"—Nevin
Theme: Scherzo, from "A Midsummer Night's Dream"—Mendelssohn

p. 138 *Contrasting Dances*
Theme: Mazurka, from the ballet "Coppelia"—Delibes
Theme: Gavotte, "Amaryllis"—Ghys
Theme: Dance of the Happy Spirits—Gluck. See Theme on page 144.

p. 179 *The Hungarian Gypsies Dance for Brahms*
Theme: Hungarian Dance No. 5—Brahms
Theme: Hungarian Dance No. 6—Brahms
Theme: Farandole, from "L'Arlésienne" Suite—Bizet. See song on page 174.

B. Listening should be directly related to and associated with the other experiences in the five-fold music activities program. Progress within the listening program itself consists of a series of step-ups to music of increasingly higher artistic levels. Listening should be a creative experience, involving observation, imagination, discrimination, and comparison. The relationship with the other fields of activity may be indicated as follows:

1. Listening and the singing program.
   a. The pupils should hear artistic performances of their own songs by selected groups of children, by experienced singers, and from recordings.
   b. Folk songs and widely familiar songs help to associate music with peoples, events, and places.
   c. Art songs expand the conception of beautiful songs well sung.

2. Listening and the rhythmic program.
   a. Songs and instrumental music for dancing.
   b. Ballets and other artistic music for dancing.
   c. Art music based on dance rhythms and forms.

3. Listening and the instrumental program.
   a. Music with which to play their percussion instruments.
   b. Music for solo instruments.
   c. Music for instrumental ensembles.

4. Listening and the creative program. Beautiful examples of the styles of various composers and of the simpler dance and song forms.

VI. CREATING

All of the phases of the creative program initiated in the primary grades are continued and expanded in the intermediate grades. In the field of melodic invention a significant step-up occurs. In the primary grades the children are encouraged to give spontaneous expression to their emotional reactions in brief melodic fragments set to their own words, about things which awakened their interest. In the intermediate grades an organized program of melodic invention is presented, based on the recognized principles of musical composition. It makes clear in the simplest way that the composer must be artisan as well as artist. The pupil realizes this fact and thereby acquires a clearer insight into the ways and meanings of musical expression.

A. Creative interpretation. Every song learned becomes an occasion for creative interpretation, in which the pupils participate in determining the way in which it should be sung.

B. Adding original stanzas:
   pp. 8, 35, 115

C. Creative activities:
   pp. 16, 86a, 87, 109, 155, 161, 174, and the program of RHYTHMIC ACTIVITIES.

D. Creative instrumentation:
   pp. 79, 164

E. Creative listening. See the LISTENING program.

F. Inventing songs and instrumental melodies.
   1. Phrase pattern forms: pp. 4, 7, 71, 116, 117
   2. Example: p. 69
   3. Free invention: pp. 4, 71, 117, 142
   4. Melodies set to given verses: pp. 71, 116, 117, 142

CLASSIFIED INDEX

ACKNOWLEDGMENTS

(Cont'd from p. ii)

William A. Owens for "Tideo" from *Swing and Turn: Texas Play-Party Games,* published by the Tardy Publishing Company.

G. Ricordi & Co., Inc., for "Butterflies" from *I Canti Della Montagna,* copyright, 1929, and "How Grows the Bulb" from *Songs for Children,* Vol. II.

Bertha E. Roberts and Aneta T. Beckman for "A Prayer" and "The Sunset" from *Children's Voices,* published by Silver Burdett Company.

Jessie Rittenhouse Scollard for "A Rain Song" by Clinton Scollard from *A Boy's Book of Verse.*

Charles Scribner's Sons for permission to reprint the words of "This Is the Day the Child Was Born" from *Eighteen Poems by James Boyd.*

María Solano for the Spanish version of "Lullaby" from *Cuentos y Lecturas en Castellano,* published by Silver Burdett Company.

Jean Thomas and Joseph A. Leeder for "Pawpaw Patch" from *The Singin' Gatherin',* published by Silver Burdett Company.

Henri Wehrmann for "Across the Bayou" and "Waltzing."

Yale University Press for permission to reprint the words of "Chanticleer" from *Songs for Parents* by John Farrar.

ALPHABETIC INDEX

11 12 13 14 15—BK—59 58 57 56 55 54 53